# AN INTRODUCTION

# OBTAINING THE VIEWS OF USERS OF HEALTH SERVICES

---

## Shirley McIver

### Consumer Feedback Resource

King's Fund Centre
Quality Improvement Programme

March 1991

King's Fund Centre for Health Services Development

Published by
King's Fund Publishing
11–13 Cavendish Square
London W1M 0AN

First published 1991
Reprinted 1992, 1996

ISBN 0 903060 85 X

A CIP catalogue record for this book is available from the British Library

Distributed by Bournemouth English Book Centre (BEBC)
PO Box 1496
Poole
Dorset
BH12 3YD
Tel: 0800 262260
Fax: 0800 262266

Printed and bound in Great Britain

# Contents

# PREFACE

This publication is the first in a series aimed at helping health service staff to obtain the views of service users, and it is written for anyone who has been given this responsibility, whether nursing, medical, paramedical or managerial. It presumes no social science background and offers a basic introduction to the subject, including discussion of the concept of 'patient satisfaction' and the description of an approach which avoids some of the pitfalls associated with this complex area.

What is offered here is a practical guide to enable health care professionals to decide *who* they want to get feedback from, *why* they want to do it, *how* they want to do it, and *in what way* they can ensure that service improvements occur as a result.

This book is produced by the Consumer Feedback Resource, an information and advice service aimed at improving feedback techniques, disseminating information about current projects and examples of good practice, networking, and building up a source of data about patient views and experiences.

# ACKNOWLEDGEMENTS

I would like to thank my colleagues in the Quality Improvement Programme at the King's Fund Centre; and Tessa Brooks in particular, for comments on a draft version of the book. Thanks to Alex Greenwood for help with gathering information. Thanks also to Madeleine Rooke-Ley for typing up the manuscript.

# 1 INTRODUCTION

It is no longer a novel idea for health care providers to want to obtain the views of service users. Encouraged by government publications such as the Griffiths Report in 1983, and more recently the White Paper *Working for Patients* in 1989, health care providers at all levels, whether Regional, District or Unit, are keen to improve service quality in ways which reflect the needs and views of users and the wider public. Despite this acceptance of the need to do so, however, the process of obtaining user views is proving to be a complicated and sometimes problematic activity for health care providers. The will may be there but knowledge of the way is often lacking.

That this is so is not really surprising because techniques for use in a health care setting cannot be developed overnight. Until recently, social research on patients was mainly conducted either by academics who had their own agenda of importance, and whose aims and objectives were not necessarily of interest to health care providers; or by Community Health Councils, whose agenda was closer to that of health care providers, but who because they lacked funds or were inexperienced frequently produced reports which were unconvincing or difficult to act upon.

Apart from one or two exceptions, such as Winifred Raphael at the King's Fund Centre and Ann Cartwright at the Institute for Social Studies in Medical Care in the 1970s, it is only during the latter part of the 1980s that academics have become more closely involved with developing survey instruments to obtain the information required by health care providers (eg the UWIST/HPAU inpatient questionnaire 'What the Patient Thinks'). Consequently the scientific development of these instruments is in its infancy.

There are two elements in the process of developing techniques and instruments for use by health care providers to obtain the views of service users, which although intertwined benefit from separate examination. These elements are that the instruments must provide information which is both *accurate* and *useful*. The information obtained must reflect the views, experiences or opinions of service users, but must also be information which relates to issues considered important by service providers, and must be collected in a way which enables them to make changes to improve service quality.

## Accuracy

In order to collect accurate information about user views, a number of conceptual and methodological issues have to be resolved. These include:

★   obtaining a representative sample of users

★   asking the right questions

★   asking questions in an appropriate manner

★   understanding and interpreting the data correctly.

All of these issues will be addressed in the following chapters, but one in particular needs to be examined at the outset. This is related to 'asking the right questions' and concerns the concept of *satisfaction*.

Many health service staff who wish to obtain user views are now, quite rightly, concerned about the validity of the 'patient satisfaction survey'. This type of survey is usually one in which patients are given a self-completion questionnaire with questions asking 'Were you satisfied with ... (or 'How satisfied were you with ...) some aspect of the service?' – and the patient is required to tick a yes/no box or a graded scale ranging from 'very satisfied' to 'very dissatisfied'.

There are a number of problems associated with questions asked in this way. Not the least of these, as Locker and Dunt (1978) point out, is that it is rare to find the concept of satisfaction defined. There has been little clarification of what the term means, to either health care providers or service users.

Some researchers have suggested that patient satisfaction is related to prior expectations (Stimson and Webb, 1975; Cartwright, 1964; Tessler and Mechanic, 1975; Larsen and Rootman, 1976; Korch, Gozzi and Francis, 1968) although the relationship is not clear. Other research has produced results which question the extent to which patients have strong expectations prior to treatment (Fitzpatrick and Hopkins, 1983).

It seems likely that different patients will have expectations which vary in concreteness and strength and that this variation will relate to their knowledge and prior experience and so will change over time and with service use. If this is the case, and if satisfaction is related to these changing expectation, it makes the measurement of satisfaction a complex task.

Even if satisfaction is connected to expectation in a direct and simple way (for example, if low expectation produces high levels of satisfaction, as seems to be the case with the elderly) it poses problems. It may be accurate information but what *use* is it? What does it mean? Is the service of good quality or not? Should expectations be raised through a process of patient education? Should the views of those with low expectations be discounted?

Asking service users about their satisfaction with a service is asking them to *evaluate* that service. It is asking them to make a judgement about how good they thought it was. A service is made up of many different parts: for example, making an appointment and getting to it (access); waiting time; waiting environment and/or facilities when admitted (hotel services); receptionists' manner; nurses' interpersonal and technical skill; the consultation or treatment provided by medical staff; leaving after an appointment or being discharged (follow up and continuity of care). All of these parts of a service are important and require separate evaluation. It may be that the different parts can be ranked as more or less important parts of the total service by different individuals, but improving service quality is not about improving one aspect of a service at the expense of another.

The development of instruments measuring patient satisfaction – that is, those which ask patients to evaluate part of a service – is in its early stages in Britain, and service providers who wish to develop such instruments should seek advice from a social scientist with expertise in this field. This does not mean that relatively simple instruments which provide useful information cannot be developed. The Richmond Rehabilitation Unit for the Elderly has developed a postal questionnaire to assess patients' views of the physiotherapy service and this includes questions which ask patients to evaluate the service and outcome of treatment. However the wording carefully avoids the term 'satisfaction' and takes account of expectations, in questions such as 'In the light of your expectations before treatment, were the results: disappointing; as expected; better than expected; or were you unable to judge?' The type of questions and the style of presentation used seem to have worked well with these particular service users, as an 86 per cent response rate was achieved, which for a postal questionnaire is very good indeed (McCallum, 1990).

In the USA more work has been carried out on the development of measures of patient satisfaction, and a review published by the US Congress Office of Technology Assessment (Ware, Davies and Rubin, 1988) summarises the reliability, validity and feasibility of various patient rating methods. Other studies have compared the relative strengths of two or more of these measures in assessing patient satisfaction in the same patient sample (Roberts and Tugwell, 1987).

Anyone thinking of using instruments developed in the USA, though, should proceed cautiously, as reviews indicate that they 'vary widely in design, content, administration, and overall sophistication' (Nelson and Niederberger, 1990). Errors of judgement could easily be made. For example, one of the characteristics of patients' assessment of service quality is that they generally give high ratings. On a scale of 1 to 100, for instance, they will typically give scores of 82 or above. Research in the USA has shown, however, that small differences – even at the upper end of the scale – have important implications for patients' subsequent behaviour with respect to health and health care. In one study mentioned by Kaplan and Ware (1989), an 8 point difference in patient satisfaction with care at the upper end of a scale ranging from 1 to 100 was associated with a 10-fold increase in the probability of patients' disenrollment from a health care plan. In any case, where judgements about those aspects of care which relate to the skills of nursing and medical staff are concerned, these will have to be taken in the context of outcome of treatment to have any implications for the improvement of quality in this area of service. For example, a patient may judge the nursing and medical care received during a hospital stay to have been of very high quality, but if an unnecessary operation has been performed or he/she was subsequently readmitted owing to complications arising from a too early discharge, then the patient may have made an error of judgement because he or she was not in possession of all the facts.

To ask patients for judgements about the *process* of their care, as has been discussed above, is a different issue to that of asking them about the *outcome* of that care, although the two issues are connected. Patients can provide information about their health status (how the illness affects the quality of their life) before and after medical intervention and this can be a variable in measuring the outcome of treatment. For discussion about such instruments and an example, see Stewart, Hays and Ware (1988).

Asking patients to make judgements about the process of their care can also be separated from asking them about the service they *need*. Locker and Dunt (1978) describe a pilot study they carried out on the health and social care of the elderly, where approximately 10 per cent of respondents reported that they required more help to perform a variety of tasks than was currently received from formal or informal providers, yet only 2 per cent reported that they were dissatisfied. The respondents rationalised this inconsistency by stating that although the service did not fully meet their needs, the provider was doing all that could be expected.

In sum, studies of patient satisfaction must be clear about what it is they are measuring. Are they measuring satisfaction with the service the patient is receiving? Are they trying to find out whether patients are getting the service they need? Or are they trying to measure the outcome of care?

The complexity of attempting to ask patients to make evaluations about the care they receive has undermined many service providers' confidence in the 'patient satisfaction survey'. This caution is healthy but it does not mean that health care providers should stop trying to obtain information from service users.

## Alternatives to the Patient Satisfaction Measure

Information about service users' experiences, views and opinions can be collected without confronting the problems associated with their making evaluations and judgements, and this information can be very useful in locating aspects of service delivery which are of poor quality. An account of what it is like to experience a service from the patients' point of view allows the service provider to make their own judgement about how good it is, and these accounts can really be eye-openers for staff: the patient does not have to make a judgement – either the events speak for themselves, or the distress/pleasure is obvious.

In other words, a sophisticated patient satisfaction measure is not necessary in order to obtain information about user experiences and views, and to make changes to improve service quality from the user perspective. A certain amount of knowledge and expertise *is* necessary however, and the following chapters provide advice on how to go about this task, which essentially involves:

★ exploring the service users' agenda of importance through interviews, critical incident technique, discussion groups, liaison officers, or advisory groups comprising users and/or representatives from voluntary and self-help organisations (such as MIND, Age Concern etc)

★ finding out the experiences and views of a representative number of users by constructing, piloting and then administrating a questionnaire, interview schedule or discussion checklist, or by using critical incident technique, with a sample of users

★ feeding the information obtained into a management process which allows the staff concerned with service delivery to get closer to the views and experiences of their customers, and take the lead in making changes to improve service quality.

The above discussion has been about obtaining accurate information from service users: specifically, the issue of *asking the right questions*. The point made is that although it is difficult to ask the right questions to obtain *judgements* about services from users, because this science is still in its infancy, it *is* possible to ask users the right questions about their views and experiences. The right questions in this case will emerge from exploratory interviews or research to find out the issues users consider important (for example, research frequently highlights the importance of privacy, being treated as an individual, getting enough time with the consultant, being provided with enough information, knowing what will happen next), plus the formulation of these questions in an unambiguous manner.

## Usefulness

Asking questions which elicit accurate information will not automatically obtain information which is useful as well. Data are either accurate or not, but usefulness is always connected to an aim or purpose – it is useful *for* something. Accurate data which are not also useful will produce the response 'Well that's very interesting …' but no direct implications for service provision.

Research carried out by the Centre for Health Economics, York University, in 1988 (Carr-Hill, McIver and Dixon, 1989) showed that health service managers often have difficulty making use of information obtained from surveys. Many reasons have been given for this lack of action. Some of the following may well strike a familiar chord.

★   The survey was never finished, as time and money ran out before the data could be analysed.

★   The survey results were produced but arrived after the committee meeting to decide on action had passed.

★ The survey was criticised by senior or medical staff as 'unscientific' and so the results were dismissed as unimportant.

★ The survey results failed to answer the questions which prompted it originally.

★ The survey results raised other more important questions requiring further research to answer them.

★ Staff involved were not motivated or committed to making changes suggested by the report.

★ The person who had the original idea to conduct the survey had left and no one remaining was interested in it.

A well planned and executed survey or other type of user feedback exercise can overcome these problems and produce information which will help to improve service quality from the user perspective. For this to happen, however, there must be a willingness amongst all staff to change from an organisation which historically 'knows best' what its users need, to one in which users can participate in decisions about their care.

Whether the feedback from users will be useful or not is directly connected to the issue of organisational change. That is, the development of a customer service oriented culture.

## What is a Customer Service Oriented Culture ?

Harris (1978) uses the term 'patient orientation' and defines it as the 'extent to which the health care organisation is aware of, has concern for, and is responsive to the patient as a "whole" person … Such a view implies attitudes, knowledge, and behaviour on the part of the organisational staff member appropriate for meeting the patient's needs'.

In more detail this means that staff may vary along the following dimensions:

★ **Attitudes** – from low empathy and respect to a very high concern

★ **Knowledge** – from poorly informed to well informed about the patients' experiences, needs and expectations

★ **Behaviour** – from treating patients as nuisances who must be tolerated to treating them as high priority and making significant effort to meet their needs.

Harris's article describes an action research project carried out in the USA in which the above issues were taken on board and staff ownership of the customer feedback project was considered to be the key issue. Staff ownership has also been found to be a vital aspect of service improvement projects in Britain. Those whose aim is lasting change also focus on setting up a quality management system which is built upon an all-embracing philosophy about quality.

The following chapters deal with questions surrounding the collection of user information which is both accurate and useful: Chapters 2, 4 and 5 deal with the former in particular, and Chapters 3, 6 and 7 with the latter, although in practice the two elements are intertwined.

# 2 TYPES OF SERVICE USER

Discussions about health service users always seem to draw debate about what users should be called: customers, consumers, patients, clients etc. Much of this conflict is over whether users of public services are consumers or not (see, for example, Potter, 1988; White et al, 1988), but it can be argued that both customer and consumer are applicable (McIver and Carr-Hill, 1989).

For practical purposes it matters little what service users are called. Of more importance to those health service staff who have been given the responsibility for obtaining feedback from users is how to obtain *accurate* and *useful* information. This task demands the right understanding of who service users are, rather than the right terminology: not *what* they are, but *who* they are. The difference between users is often more important than the similarity, when considering the process of obtaining feedback.

# Important Differences Between Users

What kinds of differences are important? There are four main types which will affect the process of obtaining feedback in significant ways.

## Whether a Current User or Not

The human memory is not usually very accurate and so it is wise to expect useful information only from current or *very* recent users (within two weeks of discharge or seeing a GP). Our memory of experiences becomes distorted and vague very quickly.

## Types of Service Being Used

Patients with different types of illness will have different expectations, based upon their prior knowledge of how an illness will affect a person. The type of illness they are suffering from may also affect them – not just if they are feeling too ill to respond but also because if they see their illness as life threatening, this may influence their perception of what happens to them. Some types of service user may find it particularly difficult to respond to questions about their experiences and views: for example, those suffering from a mental illness, those with severe learning difficulties, and those with certain types of physical handicap.

Relatives, companions, carers and other agencies and departments can also be service users to some extent. That is, they may use a particular aspect of a service: for example, relatives may wait with patients, carers may follow instructions about medication and lifestyle, GPs may book appointments. These partial users of services may also have different views because of their different relationships with a service.

## Social Category

Very few people like being put into a social category but sometimes these are necessary because they can highlight differences between people which will probably affect their views, experiences and expectations. It is possible to argue over which categories are most useful or relevant but traditionally those thought to make the most appropriate distinctions between people are those relating to sex, age, socio-economic status (job and financial position) and cultural background (usually ethnic group or religion).

## Knowledge of NHS Culture

Health service culture can be thought of as encompassing all that individuals learn when they work in the NHS: a knowledge of organisational structures, of the process of delivering a service, of how to do their job etc. Obviously this knowledge will vary depending on the job, but much of it will be shared.

This knowledge is related to a particular institution (the NHS) and institutions embody many of the dominant values and beliefs of the wider society. For this reason, groups which do not share these values and beliefs are also likely to lack an understanding of health service culture. Values and beliefs are part of our 'taken for granted' understanding of the world and form the basis for shared knowledge.

It is useful to think of this understanding as a continuum stretching between full knowledge of the NHS at one extreme and no knowledge at the other. Although it is unlikely that anyone will fall at the extremes, different categories of people will fall at different points along the continuum. For example, patients who also work in the NHS, and internal customers, will have a very good knowledge of the culture and take many things for granted; whereas those who have lived most of their life in another country and speak another language will have very little knowledge and the whole process of using the NHS will be strange to them.

This can affect the service providers' understanding of a person's responses, but also – more drastically – it may mean that the person will not follow medical advice correctly, or may not use a service they need, or may use it inappropriately. A particularly vivid and interesting account of how this can happen is given in 'Evil Eye or Bacteria: Turkish Migrant Workers and Swedish Health Care' (Sachs, 1987). See also Fitzpatrick and Scambler (1984).

Dividing service users into different types and categories can be a mixed blessing unless the *dual nature of categorisation* is appreciated. Categorisation can be both:

★ a useful way of *drawing attention* to important differences and similarities between groups of people, so that their views and experiences can be better understood

★ a way of *avoiding* the issues which concern certain groups of people – because labels such as 'mentally handicapped', 'epileptic', 'disabled', 'elderly' or 'black' can bring with them a set of expectations and attitudes which can hinder understanding.

Our 'taken for granted' views about different types of people are not always correct. It is essential to find out what evidence exists to support these views. The question of what counts as evidence will be examined in the section dealing with methods. A useful recent article discussing labelling of patients is 'Professional Labelling' by Anne Rourke in *Nursing Standard*, 11 July 1990, Vol. 4, No. 42.

In sum, categorisation can be helpful if it enables us to think more clearly about how the process of collecting useful and accurate information might be affected by different types of service user.

All four of the main differences between users described above will affect the process of obtaining user views: for example, in the timing of interviews and questionnaires – whether they are completed in a person's home or as they leave after their appointment or stay in hospital. In some cases this consideration may seriously jeopardise a survey: in a survey of the general population, for instance, it would be unwise to expect enough people to be able to give useful comments about particular types of services.

# Different Approaches for Different Types of User

One of the most important ways in which the different types of service user will affect the process of obtaining feedback is in the consideration of which method to use. Not all methods work equally well with everyone, and certain groups of users who are not usually asked for their views may nevertheless be able to give them if asked in the right way. A number of examples are given below.

## Children

Children are rarely asked for their views on what it was like to use a service, yet they are perfectly capable of describing experiences. Excellent guidelines for the care of children in hospitals have been drawn up by the National Association for the Welfare of Children in Hospital (NAWCH), but getting children's views can also be important in the monitoring of service standards. However, the age of the child is an important factor which will influence the approach.

At seven years old and below children are distressed by any separation from parents or normal home life and have little understanding of what is happening to them. This means that it is usually necessary to use a trained child psychologist, and it is probably more convenient to interview the parents or get the parents to ask the child questions.

From the age of eight years most children are willing to give their views, although questionnaires will have to be made interesting and attractive, as well as easy to understand. One way of approaching the subject is to construct an activity booklet for the child to read and complete. This can include games and information as well as questions about their stay and space to write or draw pictures about their experiences. Play leaders already engage children in these kinds of activities and would be able to design a children's activity booklet or pack with the aim of eliciting information about a child's use of a service.

Apart from affecting *the way* views are collected, consideration of the type of user also helps focus attention on the special needs of these different categories. Children obviously need a slightly different environment to adults and this is frequently not recognised even when children form a large percentage of service users. For example, children are the biggest single user group of A & E (30 per cent), yet there are often few facilities for them in A & E departments (Walker, 1989).

Furthermore, children are the adults of the future and so it is wise to encourage schools to prepare children for possible hospital visits as early as possible, to minimise fear and anxiety and to promote accurate expectations.

## Elderly People

Those who are elderly, particularly those suffering from dementia or the very infirm, are also a group not usually asked for their views. Although important and relevant information can be obtained from carers, it is also possible to question the elderly people themselves, and an example of this is the work done by the National Consumer Council for their publication *Consulting Consumers in the NHS: A Guideline Study* (1990). See also Elaine Cameron and Helen Evers of the Department of Social Medicine, Birmingham University, in 'Waiting to be Served', *The Health Service Journal*, 11 January 1990, pp. 54–55.

Self-completion questionnaires and similar types of survey do not usually work with the elderly, whether confused or not, because many are arthritic or have impaired vision. In any case elderly people often find it much easier to talk about their experiences in an interview situation than to respond to the impersonal format of a questionnaire.

Observation is another appropriate (though little used) method for investigating the delivery of services to elderly people. The elderly tend to have much lower expectations than younger people and surveys often pick up this uncritical attitude. Observation is a way of getting to the actual experiences of elderly patients, and proved to be a good way of distinguishing between the care provided by two nursing homes and a geriatric ward in a study by Clark and Bowling (1989).

## Black and Minority Service Users

The questionnaire survey method is not usually appropriate where black and minority users are concerned, even when translated into the appropriate language. This is because self-completion questionnaires only cater to those who can read the language they speak; and even where people are literate in English, cultural differences may make understanding the question or interpreting the reply problematic.

Also the questionnaire format perpetuates the distance between provider and receiver of health care and so does not encourage better communication, which is necessary in order to overcome the understandable suspicion of black and minority users that their views are not important.

Alternative methods such as discussion groups, panels and advisory groups will probably yield more useful information, but it is more difficult to persuade most people to give up 2–3 hours of their time to take part in a discussion group than it is to get them to spend 15 minutes filling in a questionnaire. For this reason it is particularly important that health authorities should have a well established relationship with the local black and minority communities before attempting to set up groups or panels.

Health authorities wanting to develop good relationships with these communities are likely to have:

★   an equal opportunities policy

★   staff training for working in a multi-racial society

★   information on the different black and minority groups living in the area

★   formal links with black and minority communities (eg a black and minority working party/liaison group)

★   informal links with black and minority groups (eg a development worker who has built up good contacts with local people)

★   a record of having made changes as a result of information obtained from services users.

Where good working relationships have not yet developed, it is probably more productive to use patient advocates or appropriate interviewers to explore the experiences and views of black and minority users.

## Those Suffering from a Mental Illness

Until 1985 relatively little research had been carried out to investigate the views of users of mental health services. *Index Medicus* listed an average of around ten papers per year on psychiatric topics under the heading 'consumer satisfaction', and 90 per cent of these were by American writers (Shields, 1985).

One reason for this lack of research was a concern that the views collected from a survey might not be reliable because of distortions caused by the patient's state of mind. To cope with this anticipated problem many surveys also included some measurement of the psychological state of the patient. However, Winifred Raphael addressed the question of reliability in her survey published in 1977, and she found that only 2 per cent of patients who responded failed to give rational answers and only 3 per cent handed in very incomplete questionnaires (Raphael, 1977).

Although Raphael's survey has been widely used, problems associated with the survey method are increased with this client group. These include the difficulty of obtaining a random sample (many patients are reluctant to take part in surveys as they are worried about confidentiality), and the difficulty of conducting post-discharge surveys (mental health service users returning to the community can be difficult to trace because many have itinerant lifestyles). Also service providers may feel obliged to omit certain people in order to avoid appearing insensitive or arousing distress: for instance, those who have been re-referred or those who are known to have left the service with feelings of acrimony. Providers may also be hesitant about carrying out interviews with these users to establish their agenda of importance. Certainly few of the existing questionnaires appear to have been developed following interviews.

An approach which may stand a better chance of finding out the user's view of mental health services is that of patient advocacy, which started in Holland in the early 1970s. A number of advocacy organisations now exist in the mental health field, the most well known being the Nottingham Patients' Council Support Group (see Chapter 4 for further details).

It *may* be possible to design questionnaires or interview schedules based upon information obtained from advocacy groups if the aim is to obtain the views of a representative sample of users, but even so the other problems associated with the survey method will still exist. Only experience will tell whether the self-confidence building work of advocacy groups will help to overcome the understandable suspicion with which surveys are viewed by many users of mental health services. In any case, an advocacy group may be the most effective way to improve service quality for these service users.

## People with Learning Difficulties

This client group is one which is often thought of as having communication difficulties, and consequently as being unable to express views about service use. Fortunately this does not appear to be the case.

The questionnaire survey is probably the method least likely to succeed in eliciting information from this type of user, although West Surrey and North East Hampshire Health Authority are piloting a questionnaire based upon the 'oucher' system, which uses a series of faces showing a variety of expressions. More usual are interviews, such as the semi-structured interview schedule used by Aylesbury Vale Health Authority, Quality of Life Review Group, in 1989. Advocacy groups also exist which help people with learning difficulties to speak for themselves. The Norah Fry Research Centre at the University of Bristol has a research project looking at people with learning difficulties involved in self-advocacy and citizen advocacy, as well as other projects involving this client group.

Those wondering whether it is possible to involve people with learning difficulties in policy and planning meetings will find Whittaker (1990) very useful.

## Outpatients

Outpatient departments attract high levels of patient dissatisfaction – the 1984 report *British Social Attitudes* found that 21 per cent of the population surveyed expressed varying degrees of dissatisfaction with this part of the service, compared with 7 per cent and 13 per cent with inpatient services and GPs respectively (Jowell and Airey, 1984). Yet outpatient users have been surveyed widely for many years. A study carried out by the Centre for Health Economics, University of York, in 1988 (Carr-Hill, McIver and Dixon, 1989) found that surveys of outpatient departments were the third largest category of survey after inpatients and maternity. So what has gone wrong? If surveys have been able to locate problems why have changes not taken place to make service users more satisfied?

One reason is that problems such as long waiting times are often difficult to tackle, although some hospitals are now having success after changing the appointment system and informing waiting patients about delays. Another is that the outpatient department is not really one department but an area where a number of different services work, in which there is often no overall co-ordination and no one individual has clear responsibility for making changes; indeed changes often require co-operation from a number of different services.

The questionnaire survey can be a useful tool for monitoring outpatient views and experiences but there are still many questionnaires which do not draw upon the patients' agenda of importance. A number of studies have investigated this agenda using in-depth interviews – North West Thames Regional

Health Authority, for example, used critical incident technique to inform *Managing Customer Relations* (1986). It is important to remember that questionnaires are not necessarily appropriate for monitoring every aspect of the outpatient service, and an approach which combines a number of methods is advisable (McIver, 1991).

# Customer Related Questions to Ask Before Starting a Feedback Exercise

★ How much understanding does the user group have of health service culture?

★ Is the user group homogenous, or does it consist of a number of different levels of understanding?

★ Are the views of all types of users in the target group of interest, or only some?

★ Are there community groups, voluntary organisations or similar sources of help to enable you to get information from the service users concerned?

★ What information already exists about the experiences and views of those service users you are interested in?

# 3 AIMS

It is essential that the reasons for the collection of information from service users are clear because this could influence choice of method. Different methods produce different types of information. If you know *what* you want and *why* you want it, you are more likely to *use* the information you collect.

Information about service users, including their views and experiences, is likely to be collected during a number of different activities. These activities are really different stages of a general cycle of service development and appraisal, but it is useful to look at some of them individually in order to see how different types of information may be required.

One way of categorising these activities is by considering the extent to which they make use of information provided by service users rather than service providers. At one extreme are activities which require very little information from service users, at the other those for which a large amount of information is required. Public relations work appears to lie at the former extreme, while planning service provision lies at the latter, demanding much information from service users. Other activities such as patient education, service review and progressive monitoring of service effectiveness require more information from users. This point can be made clearer by examining a number of activities in turn.

# Planning Service Provision

This is the activity which probably requires most information from current and potential service users. A wide range of information is desirable and so a variety of methods will be necessary in order to obtain answers to the questions raised.

There will be a need for statistical information (such as number of potential users, their socio-economic categories, age etc) and narrative information (such as how they would prefer to receive the service), which can be collected through methods such as analysis of records, projected demographic statistics, questionnaire surveys, interviews and discussion groups.

Current and potential service users could also take part in planning meetings where they would be valuable in helping to keep customers to the forefront and helping to locate areas where public resistance to changes may occur. However, it is likely that such involvement in planning will only work where support is provided for users. That is, help to understand the information they will be expected to assimilate, and knowledge about the way planning meetings operate.

# Setting Service Standards

Setting standards is part of the wider process of quality assurance. The term quality assurance generally applies to an organisation-wide management system designed to collect and assess information about quality of service.

Service standards will generally be set by professionals but it is difficult to see how they can accomplish their task without *some* input from the recipients of their service. In each area of structure, process and outcome, the service user will have preferences. The problem is that the preferences of service users may be based upon low expectations, or an unrealistic view of what is possible.

This means that any involvement of service users in standard' setting is heavily dependent upon their being provided with information. It is likely that only groups which already have access to much of this information (eg voluntary organisations like MIND) will be useful initially, unless service providers are willing to encourage the setting up of working groups involving users, and then provide these groups with plenty of help and support to enable them to make decisions about what it is realistic to aim for.

Methods such as questionnaire surveys are not generally useful in the *development* of service standards unless the questions are based upon extensive prior research to find out what service users consider to be relevant standards, or the questionnaire is part of a larger data collection exercise. For example, Leeds Western Health Authority used an analysis of written complaints, the results of a 3 month pilot suggestion scheme, and the results of consumer surveys to identify 80 quality indicators. Staff were also asked to identify indicators. The resultant combined 88 quality indicators were then listed and users were asked to tick the 20 they thought most important. A total of 1,057 people – current NHS service users, potential users (through the library service), and members of self-help groups – were involved. These priority indicators, a large proportion of which are related to providing consumers with information and involving them in their own care, now form the basis of a service checklist and questionnaire which staff are being asked to complete. The aim is to try and assess the extent to which services are meeting the quality indicators identified by service users.

The Leeds Western example relates to the development of general service standards, but users can also be usefully involved in the development of standards relating to specific services and particular types of illness. An example of the latter is the protocol developed by City and Hackney Health Authority for dealing with sufferers of sickle cell disease.

# Monitoring Service Standards

The measuring and monitoring of standards involves a continual assessment of how a service is performing and is heavily dependent upon feedback from service users. The object of the exercise is for management to receive a *regular* flow of feedback from service users and providers. This feedback can take many forms, but given that it needs to generate information which can be processed quickly, methods which involve time consuming analysis are not very productive.

There are two main ways in which consumers can be involved in service monitoring:

★   as providers of information about user experiences

★   as part of a monitoring panel/group.

The first approach is the standard way users are involved, although there are problems connected to finding a method which can produce continuous feedback. Survey methods run into difficulties because information processing is generally too slow, but the CASPE team at the King's Fund College have devised a method using a short standard questionnaire and an optical reader which speeds up the process. It is currently being piloted in six DHAs. Short, specific and easily analysed questionnaires are essential.

Other appropriate methods would be regular discussion forums with groups of users; an 'independent' customer liaison officer, who systematically walked wards and service areas talking to patients, making notes and building up a file of information about problems/complaints/satisfaction/misunderstandings etc and who wrote regular reports for management; and clearly marked suggestion boxes in areas well used by the public (perhaps also with information about how to make a complaint) – the contents of these to be examined regularly. If suggestion boxes do not produce information it may also be necessary to designate a 'customer relations officer' to spend time in public areas talking to users and staff and encouraging them to use the boxes.

The second way service users can be involved in monitoring is by being part of a monitoring panel. That is, a group of people who are responsible for obtaining information about the day to day running of a particular service, and who meet regularly to discuss progress. In this instance, information can come from a variety of sources – those mentioned above, plus discussions with staff, observation, and examination of regularly produced statistical information.

## Service Evaluation

Whereas monitoring is carried out frequently to assess continuous performance, service evaluation takes place at regular intervals to determine how effectively the original aims determined during service planning are being met.

Service evaluation demands a very wide range of information relating to questions such as 'Does the service do what it was set up to do?' and 'What is it like to use?'. The diagram shown in Figure 1 (overleaf), developed by the National Consumer Council, may help to illustrate the type of information it is necessary to collect (National Consumer Council, 1986).

Feedback from consumers is an important part of service evaluation, along with feedback from staff and the examination of other types of information, such as that collected during service monitoring.

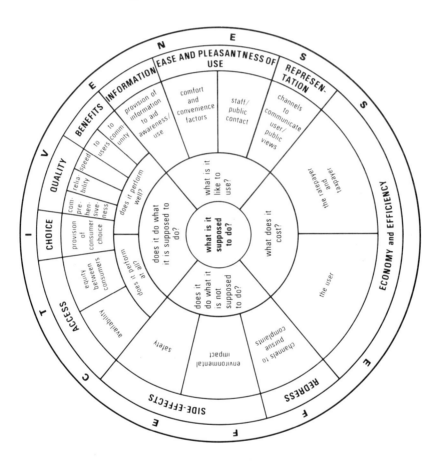

Figure 1.  Consumer criteria for service evaluation.

(Taken from: National Consumer Council, *Measuring Up: Consumer Assessment of Local Authority Services – A Guideline Study*, 1986.)

A variety of methods will be necessary to collect the different types of information needed. The aim will be to build upon the information already available by using methods that are compatible with the questions remaining unanswered. These may involve qualitative information (eg why Asian women are not using ante-natal clinics), suggesting methods such as patient advocate/liaison officer, semi-structured interviews and discussion groups; or quantitative information (eg how long patients have to wait for treatment for different illnesses, or how many accidents occur in a hospital).

It is perhaps important to point out that although users will most typically be involved in providing information which will then be examined by the evaluation team of service providers, there may also be a place for their involvement in the evaluation team. Users at this level of involvement may help the team to focus on issues of importance to the consumer. Those who are unsure about evaluation and want a 'beginners guide' may find Stocking (1990) helpful.

## Service Review

In practice service review is probably combined with service evaluation, but its aim is slightly different in that it seeks to review the service planned originally, in the light of subsequent changes. The purpose is to find out whether the original aims and intentions are still valid. Many of the questions asked during service evaluation will be relevant but the emphasis will be on assessing the impact of any changes in population or circumstances that have occurred since the original plans were made.

Again, a very wide range of information will be needed, the views and experiences of service users being of great importance. During service review it will be particularly necessary to obtain an overall picture by examining the results of evaluation and monitoring from overlapping services, or those which relate to one another.

It will be a very difficult task for user representatives to gain the amount of knowledge necessary to help with service review groups, but with support they may be able to pick up on issues that are of importance to service users, particularly if they have also been involved in related service planning teams.

# Public Relations

Public relations is about enhancing the view people have of a particular product and encouraging them to buy it in preference to one of a different brand. How can this apply to the NHS, where customer choice does not exist in the same way?

Where health authorities are concerned, market research exercises are sometimes carried out as part of public relations work 'to show people that we care about their views'. Unfortunately, finding out views is not enough as far as users are concerned: if changes are not made along the lines suggested, bad feeling is increased and the effort is counter-productive. Often feedback exercises are unnecessary in this context.

Public relations in health authorities is more usefully about persuading the public that certain changes are necessary to fulfil the aims of the NHS. In such cases it is necessary to find out what people in a certain area think about an issue, and to establish a line of communication with them, in order to know how to change their views (if necessary). That is, to sell them a service which may not benefit them directly. If a service change is inevitable, there is no point in getting feedback of the kind which asks 'What kind of changes would you prefer?'. The questions must be directed at finding out how much the relevant people *know* about the change, with the aim of increasing their knowledge and understanding. Questions can also be aimed at finding out what the arguments against the proposed changes are likely to be, so that counter-arguments can be formulated.

Public relations can also be about providing people with information through advertisements and leaflets. Much public relations work depends upon providing people with information about health services rather than obtaining information from them, so a feedback exercise will be unnecessary. On the other hand, an assessment or evaluation of the usefulness of the information provided *will* require feedback from service users as recipients of this material.

In a few instances the public's knowledge and understanding of an issue or the type of argument people may bring against a particular development may be the target of the enquiry. In these cases the appropriate methods are initial interviews and discussion groups with influential people (eg opinion leaders, community spokesmen), followed by publicity and public meetings once counter-arguments have been prepared and the level of knowledge and understanding on both sides has increased.

## Patient Education

In reality, provision of information to patients and patient education overlap considerably. Public relations and health education may be two distinct activities, but both aim to convey messages to current and future service users. Both seek to influence current and future service use: public relations by encouraging the appropriate use of services, and health education by improving self-management of illness and promoting preventative health care.

Patient education differs, however, in being more directly concerned to help specific groups of people. Thus patients who have had an illness or accident, or been subject to medical intervention (eg diabetes sufferers, or those having had a coronary or stroke) are provided with information to enable them to manage their condition. This education about self-management is also necessary for many of those disabled from birth, or the chronically sick.

Although the education process will be provider-led, some information from users is necessary for it to work successfully. For example, providers of care will need to know how to convey information so that users understand it, and what aspects of self-management are of most importance to users. On closer examination, it is apparent that the learning process is in fact a mutual one, with health care providers being told by users what it is like to experience a particular illness (or lifestyle where health education is concerned).

The information required from users in these instances is largely of the qualitative kind. Education about a specific illness often occurs after a traumatic event for the user and so counselling and support are important. A standard questionnaire is unlikely to produce the kind of information that providers will find useful. More relevant will be semi-structured interviews and possibly discussion groups (sometimes talking to others who have experienced similar events can be therapeutic, as well as providing information about experiences).

General health education is slightly different in that the aim is to persuade individuals who may not currently be ill to make changes in their lifestyle in order to decrease the risk of future illness. Not only are large numbers of individuals involved, but these individuals are likely to have widely different lifestyles. There is some advantage in using methods which collect statistical information (quantitative) as well as those which collect narrative information (qualitative) in order to uncover basic attributes which distinguish segments of the population, so that these can then be targeted with information conveyed in different ways.

# Customer Relations

Customer relations and public relations are frequently thought of as identical activities but the two can serve different functions. Public relations is about improving the public image of a health authority or hospital, especially in order to counteract bad publicity, or about persuading the public that certain types of service provision are desirable; whereas customer relations is about improving the relationship that exists between service users and providers. Customer relations is directly concerned with helping existing service users rather than influencing the general public.

This means that customer relations staff are of great importance in ensuring that health care providers are sensitive to the views of those who use their services. Although senior management must be committed to the task in order for it to succeed, customer relations staff can carry out a number of important tasks. They can co-ordinate feedback exercises and collate information, and are also able to appraise existing methods and help develop new ones by assessing feedback exercises.

In addition, they can gather much relevant information by making themselves available to service users in key areas, such as outpatient departments, and by walking around wards. By talking informally to patients about their experiences and noting down the information gained in this way, they can quickly identify problem areas and issues which need further investigation. As long as regular reports are written, and systems established which ensure that user feedback reaches those who need it, the information and knowledge will not disappear when they leave.

Customer relations personnel are also valuable in aiding communication between providers and users of services. They can facilitate discussion groups, troubleshoot, and advise on training requirements.

At present very few designated customer relations officers exist in the NHS. These tasks are often carried out by a variety of people whose main work lies elsewhere, and so customer relations tends to be piecemeal and underdeveloped. In this circumstance it is important that an outside organisation attempts to co-ordinate and develop customer relations activities. This means that those who are given customer relations responsibilities should make every effort to find out what is happening in their own and other health authorities. One way of achieving this is to contribute to a central customer feedback information resource (such as the King's Fund Consumer Feedback Resource), which can facilitate the exchange of information.

# Purchasers and Providers

Recent government changes to NHS structure are said to be directed at improving the quality of care patients receive. The separation of health authorities into purchasers (DHAs) and providers (units) will create a division in the service planning, monitoring and review cycle.

It is still not completely clear how standard setting and monitoring will work in practice, but the government document *Contracts for Health Services: Operating Contracts* (1990) suggests that providers will be primarily responsible for this task. Section 3.4 (p. 6) states that:

> The onus should be placed on providers to demonstrate precisely how they propose to meet the purchaser's requirement, and what system will be in place to assure provision to the agreed quality standards.

However, in order to satisfy the slightly earlier requirement of this section –

> Purchasers must therefore have clear objectives as to the nature and quality of services that will best meet the needs of their residents

– it is clear that purchasers will have to work out principles or general standards of service quality.

Using this guidance as a base, it is possible to draw up a list of the main customer related quality activities that purchasers and providers will each need to be engaged in.

| DISTRICT (Purchaser / Commissioner) | UNIT (Provider) |
|---|---|
| Statement of general principles/aims | Statement of general principles/aims |
| District health needs profile, including an investigation into unmet need | Service standard setting |
| Service review, including an exploration of underuse or inappropriate use of services and an examination of preferred service combinations and style of delivery | Monitoring of standards |
|  | Evaluation of performance in relation to standards |
|  | Review of standards |
| Evaluation of achievements against aims | Customer relations (with direct service users, GPs and purchasers) |
| Public relations | Public relations |

Table 1. Quality activities involving customers – following the White Paper.

Many health authorities are treating the contracting process as one of negotiation between DHA and DMUs, one in which they work together to identify ways in which the dialogue with the consumer can be improved in all areas of service delivery and at all levels, from that of the individual user, through that of user consultation and representation, to collective participation in the planning, reviewing and monitoring of services.

For example, Swindon Health Authority employed a researcher for six months to 'seek out and evaluate what has been, what is being, and what more might be done to bring to the delivery of health care the advantages of consumer involvement', and to suggest a model/framework that could assist in developing further consumer involvement, and identify a programme of subsequent action research. This approach is valuable because it has the advantage of building upon existing good practice in a systematic and comprehensive way.

# Aim Related Questions to Ask Before Starting a Feedback Exercise

★ What information do you need?

★ What questions are you asking?

★ Why do you need this information?

★ Can you get this information from anywhere else without starting a project of your own?

★ What type of information is it you need? (Statistical or narrative? Incidence or understanding? Is the number of occurrences more important than why they occur, or do you need to know both?)

★ Do you want minimal or extensive information from users?

★ Do you want users to be involved in decisions as well as information provision?

# 4 METHODS

Most NHS staff will automatically think of the 'patient satisfaction survey' when the question of obtaining user views is raised. This is not the only option. There are many other approaches and some of these can be more appropriate than the survey. The subject needs to be examined in the broader context of obtaining 'evidence'. That is, what counts as enough evidence to form the basis for change.

Different situations call for different types of evidence. The type most usually brought to mind is scientific evidence, and this is usually associated with evidence based upon scientific experiments which are designed to disprove a hypothesis about why something happens (no hypothesis can be proved to be true – see Popper, 1962). Scientific experiments are ones where all the different variables can be controlled so that a single variable can be altered at a time to examine its effect. They are usually conducted in a laboratory which is able to set up these controlled experimental conditions.

The results of scientific *experiments* are not the only type of scientific evidence, however. Rigorous data collection and analysis procedures can also produce scientific evidence. Typically these involve the meticulous observation, description and categorisation of objects, animals, events and behaviours. From this type of work hypotheses and theories are constructed, and further observations matched against these to test for fit.

Social science is the study of people in their social context and rarely takes place in a laboratory because:

★   a laboratory is a special kind of social situation, and

★   most of human social life cannot be recreated in such a setting.

Instead of this kind of laboratory research, people are investigated during their everyday activities. Various methods have been developed to examine people's views, actions, interactions, experiences, attitudes and beliefs. Disciplines such as sociology and anthropology have also constructed theories and hypotheses about why people have these views and behave as they do, about the way that people act within organisations and institutions, and about how they become socialised and pass on behaviours, customs and beliefs.

It is not relevant to discuss here the arguments over the differences between social science and natural science (see, for example, Bernstein, 1976) or whether natural science follows its own principles in practice (Mulkay, 1979) because only two basic points are being made.

1   There are available a range of tried and tested methods for investigating people, their views, experiences and expectations and like all scientific procedures these require expertise.

2   Scientific evidence is only *one* form of evidence and can be differentiated from others. For example, there is also what counts as evidence in a law court, or what counts as evidence that someone is a great writer or not, or an original artist as opposed to being merely derivative.

# What Counts as Evidence ?

All the different kinds of evidence are based upon 'facts', but what counts as a fact is a product of the discipline concerned (eg sociology, history, law etc). That is, a product of the professional organisation, its theories and rules.

So where does this leave health professionals wishing to find out the views of service users? They will obviously wish to make their work as scientific as possible by drawing upon social science methods, but *what counts as evidence for service change is not itself 'scientific'*. It is not part of that scientific study. What counts as evidence will have to be agreed upon by health professionals themselves. It will always be possible for some (at present it is usually medical staff) to say they do not accept the 'facts' as evidence; but just how many people would count as a significant number, say, where criticism about signposting is concerned? Ten people, fifty? 50 per cent within a survey, 75 per cent? To say that results are not significant is to express an opinion in this particular context, until levels of significance are agreed.

The attempt to establish what will count as evidence for service change lies behind the whole movement to set service standards and ways of monitoring these standards. These can be seen as the theories and rules behind what seems to be emerging as the professional organisation known as 'Quality Assurance in Health Care'.

Having examined the context for the use of social science methods by health professionals, it is now appropriate to discuss these methods briefly (for a more detailed examination, see Denzin, 1970). There are two main types: quantitative and qualitative.

# Quantitative Methods

These involve the collection and analysis of information in numerical form. That is, incidence or rates of occurrences – death rates, accident rates, throughput figures, the number of patients answering 'yes' to a particular question etc.

Most types of information can be translated into numbers. For example, the number of times a particular topic occurs in a newspaper during a particular week; or the number of times the phrase 'I don't understand' occurs in a conversation. Quantitative methods work best when the item is a relatively straightforward one: for example, a person's age or sex; their address; whether or not they are employed; the means by which they travelled to a clinic; whether they own various material goods such as cars, washing machines or computers. Deaths, accidents and so on may also be relatively straightforward.

Even where these apparently simple items are concerned, however, there are two things to remember. First, no statistic is completely simple, because *how it was collected* is a factor to be taken into account. Thus, what a person counts as 'an accident' and so worthy of recording may differ among people and at different times, unless the criteria for recognition are very explicit. Secondly, if the items are used as indicators of something else (eg if ownership of computers/cars/ dishwashers or place of residence are taken as indicators of wealth or socio-economic status), then there have to be multiple indicators and the relationship has be made explicit so that others can question it if necessary.

Less straightforward items cause further problems when translated into numbers. To take the example of recovery rate – one person may count themselves as 'fully recovered' from an illness where another would not, and a health professional may have yet another view. To simplify the process, what is to count as 'fully recovered' may be defined by the service provider, but this leaves open the question of how important the provider's view is relative to that of the service user.

## The Questionnaire Survey

Complex information about the views and experiences of people is difficult to collect in a form which can be translated into a number. The usual way is for the provider to ask a question and limit the response to yes/no/don't know, or to a range of replies from 'very satisfactory' to 'very unsatisfactory'. These responses can then be coded numerically and reported as the percentage of people 'saying they were satisfied with ... '. This is termed the 'pre-coded self-completion questionnaire survey' and is currently the most popular method.

## Limitations of the Questionnaire Survey

There are four main problems with the pre-coded self-completion questionnaire:

### I Agenda Setting

The agenda is usually set by health service providers who construct questions around the areas they consider to be important for patients. The service user rarely has any input into decisions about which areas are to be covered by the questions.

### II Sensitivity

The survey method is not sensitive to complex issues where an explanation from the service user may be necessary in order to make a response understandable.

## III  Selectivity

Self-completion questionnaires are generally used in surveys for ease of administration and speed, but they will not record the views of those who are illiterate, who do not read English, who cannot use their hands, or who have impaired eyesight. Also a number of people find questionnaires threatening and will refuse to complete them.

## IV  Lack of User Participation

The method is usually a one-way process in which users' views are collected but no information about the results of the survey or any changes made are fed back to them. This can perpetuate the often already existing technical approach which treats users as 'objects' (in this case of research) rather than people. Users are not involved in exploring issues, seeking solutions to problems or making decisions about service provision – processes which treat them as human beings.

# Overcoming the Limitations of the Questionnaire Survey

These problems can be overcome to a considerable extent.

## I  Agenda Setting

Issues considered important by service providers may not be those which are of most concern to service users. The service users' agenda can be discovered by conducting unstructured or semi-structured interviews before designing a questionnaire. A small number (15–20) of as wide a variety of service users as possible should be interviewed by someone experienced in the art (eg psychologists, social scientists or counsellors). During these interviews in which the experiences of service users are explored, areas of service provision which users consider to be important can be identified and investigated. These priority areas can then be reflected in the questions asked; in addition, the questions can be constructed to reflect the language users find familiar.

## II Sensitivity

A short questionnaire which covers a wide range of topics is not able to go into detail on any one topic. The amount of detail needed will depend upon whether the aim of the survey is to *explore* or *monitor* patients' views. Where the views of service users are unknown, it is best to use a sensitive method such as interviews, critical incident technique or discussion groups, rather than a structured questionnaire, so that users can 'tell it like it is'. If this type of exploration of views has already taken place and the issues and areas of concern considered important by users are already known, progress on improving service quality to meet users' needs more closely can be monitored using a questionnaire.

Short questionnaires are preferable to long ones because they are less time consuming for the patient to complete, and they are easier to analyse. Yet although the questionnaire is going to be used for monitoring, it should be designed to collect sufficient detail to enable managers to find out *in what way* a particular aspect of service provision is not meeting patients' needs. This means that a questionnaire will have to be both short and specific. That is, it will be best to construct a number of short questionnaires covering specific topics, such as access to clinic or department, quality of information provided or waiting environment.

These short questionnaires can be used in a number of different ways: *simultaneously*, to provide a 'snapshot' of user views on different aspects of the service; *alone*, to monitor a particular aspect of service delivery which is causing concern; *consecutively*, as part of a rolling programme of service monitoring; *together with other methods*, to explore a particular aspect of service delivery from a number of different angles. Short, standard questionnaires for monitoring different aspects of service delivery provide a flexible and useful tool.

## III Selectivity

Self-completion questionnaires are not always the best way to obtain information from certain types of service user. It is important to be flexible and to use questionnaires together with other approaches and methods. If the elderly, children, black and minority groups, those suffering from a mental illness or with learning difficulties or a physical disability make up a large proportion of those using the service, an alternative method should also be adopted in order to obtain the views of these groups. The use of a patient advocate or liaison officer, semi-structured interviews, observation, a discussion group, an advisory forum, or a combination of these approaches could prove an effective means of obtaining feedback.

## IV Lack of User Participation

People should be treated as human beings and not as objects or stages in a process. It is human nature to want to be involved in decision making processes where the outcome will affect our life. There are two ways to overcome this limitation. The first is to ensure that if the survey method is used, service users (and staff) are informed about results, recommendations and possible future action. This can be accomplished in many ways, from short, easy to read, and interestingly presented details about the survey displayed on notice boards in areas where service users wait, through press and radio reports, to public meetings and displays at local fairs and similar events.

The second way is to use methods which encourage more participation, such as discussion groups and advisory forums. Apart from the value to the service user, these can help service providers think issues through and develop solutions to problems.

Besides striving to overcome the limitations of the pre-coded self-completion questionnaire method, it is also important to carry out the survey in the correct way. This is not the place to go into the finer details of survey design and execution as there are a number of excellent reviews of this subject elsewhere. (For books specifically relating to health services, see Dixon and Carr-Hill, 1989; Luck, Lawrence, Pocock and Reilly, 1988; Cartwright, 1983; and Cartwright and Seale, 1990. For more general information, see Moser and Kalton, 1971; and Hoinville and Jowell, 1978.) The aim here is to discuss a number of common problems which arise when surveys are considered as a method. One of the most common worries of those who are about to conduct a questionnaire survey is that of sample size.

## Sampling

The absolute size of a sample is not as important as the number of non-respondents. The fewer of these the better because otherwise it will be difficult to know whether non-respondents have important characteristics which differentiate them from respondents and so make the sample untypical.

As a general rule, the more variation in the people who are to be given the questionnaire, the greater the sample size needs to be so that there are enough people to each category to make comparison possible.

The following table (overleaf) is a general guide to the percentage of sampling error associated with varying sample size. As can be seen, the larger the sample size, the less the error. However, the *rate of error decrease* slows down around the 400 mark, making this the most cost effective sample size given great similarity in the people who will receive the questionnaire (that is, assuming no great differences owing to ethnicity, age or social class etc).

| Sample Size | 100 | 123 | 156 | 204 | 277 | 400 | 625 | 1,100 | 2,500 | 10,000 |
|---|---|---|---|---|---|---|---|---|---|---|
| Sampling Error (%) | 10 | 9 | 8 | 7 | 6 | 5 | 4 | 3 | 2 | 1 |
| Assuming maximum heterogeneity. From Thompson, 1989. | | | | | | | | | | |

Table 2.  Inferential accuracy.

Quantitative information is useful in the right circumstances. In social science, quantitative data are used to enable generalisations to be made. A survey is often carried out after some kind of qualitative research (such as exploratory interviews or participant observation) in order to find out *how many* or *what percentage of* people have the views uncovered using the qualitative method. The health professional is not usually a social scientist and the context is not an academic one, so this method may or may not be appropriate, but there are some circumstances specific to health services in which surveys may be useful. For example, a short and specific pre-coded questionnaire can be useful for monitoring standards because it can produce results quickly. Another appropriate occasion might be where the views of the general population are being sought. The potentially large number of people who might be involved in such a project would seem to make pre-coded questionnaires necessary, but a closer examination will perhaps help to highlight some of the problems created by the health service context.

## Population Surveys

A population survey is one way of finding out the views of people who are not current users of health services. This means that it has the potential to discover the answers to a number of questions such as why those who need services are not using them, and also what new services are required.

There are many different types of population survey and so it is important to get aims and objectives clear from the start. For example, is the intention to try and get a picture of the health of the local population, or to find out about health related behaviour such as diet, exercise, alcohol use and so on? This type of local health audit has been carried out by a number of health authorities, sometimes jointly with local authorities, since the publication in 1980 of the Black Report on inequalities in health (for an update, see Smith, Bartley and Blane, 1990). For example, the Centre for Health Economics carried out a health audit for Wolverhampton Joint Consultative Committee in 1987. Currently, purchasing or commissioning authorities are most likely to be interested in this type of research. However, surveys of this kind are complicated because health status has to be related to other factors such as income, employment and housing, making complex multi-stage sampling and various sorts of correlation analysis important. Health authorities intending to carry out a district health audit are probably best advised to get specialist advice. For an example of such a survey, see the report produced by North West Thames Regional Health Authority (priced at £25 and available from 30 Eastbourne Terrace, London W2 3QR), and the report of research done for Wandsworth Health Authority (Raferty, Skingsley and Carr, 1990).

Other types of population survey can be slightly easier to design and analyse, particularly if they concern a small locality. Of sixteen population studies received by the Centre for Health Economics during a review of surveys undertaken by health authorities, most had a core of questions covering users' experiences of GPs, chemists, opticians, chiropodists, family planning clinics, the community nursing service, health services for children, health centres and maternity care services (Dixon and Carr-Hill, 1989). A recent example of such a survey is that carried out by East Dorset Community Health Council, using the postal questionnaire method. Ten thousand copies of this 163-question, eight-page questionnaire, together with Freepost reply envelopes, were sent out in January 1990. Included were questions on priorities for health care services, and proposals included in the government's White Paper *Working for Patients.* A total of 4166 questionnaires were returned and the total cost was a very reasonable £4,000. (Report available, priced at £1.00, from East Dorset Community Health Council.)

The question to ask before attempting this kind of survey is: what is the advantage in asking questions of the general population rather than current service users? It is usually better to ask current users (by handing out questionnaires in GP surgeries, chemists, health centres, to those receiving community nursing care etc) *unless* poor uptake of services or lack of knowledge about unmet need is the issue. This is because only a percentage of the general population will have recently used a health service, and for some services the number will be small. For example, it is likely that only a tiny percentage of the general population will have recently been an inpatient, although the percentage will be greater for those having recently consulted a GP.

Also if population subgroups such as the elderly, the physically disabled, children or black and minority groups are of particular concern, then a sample of the general population may not result in sufficient numbers of the subgroup required. In a case of this kind it is better to target this particular section of the population, using local community groups and/or visiting areas where they live or congregate.

Population surveys typically use either a postal questionnaire or a structured/semi-structured interview schedule method. Information about using these methods can be found in Paul Dixon and Roy Carr-Hill, *Customer Feedback Surveys: An Introduction to Survey Methods* (1989), or Mike Luck et al, *Consumer and Market Research in Health Care* (1988); but the following brief considerations may help initially.

## The Postal Questionnaire Method

When using the postal questionnaire method it is advisable to focus on one particular area of concern (eg use of GPs or of maternity services) in one questionnaire, rather than trying to cover a number of different areas at once. Long questionnaires are time consuming for users to complete, can be confusing if not expertly constructed, and can be difficult to analyse – although research has shown that length of questionnaire does not affect response rate (Jacoby, 1990). A short and specific questionnaire is most likely to yield useful information. This method will also usually require considerable effort to get a good response rate: posting two named reminders at three week intervals or telephoning/visiting a large number of non-respondents may be necessary unless the sample are very motivated to reply (as is often the case with users of maternity services). A good response rate is vital, otherwise responders may be untypical.

The postal self-completion questionnaire has a number of *advantages* over other methods.

★ It is relatively cheap to run, although the necessary chasing up of non-respondents adds to the cost.

★ It is relatively quick to complete, although sufficient time must be allowed for at least two small pilots of the questionnaire to check (1) that questions are understandable and unambiguous, and (2) that analysis of the results will answer the questions being asked or provide the information required.

★   The expertise required is located mostly at the initial stage and not throughout. That is, a skilled person needs to design and pilot the questionnaire but an administrator can collate replies, chase up non-respondents and arrange for computer coding and analysis.

The *disadvantages* of postal self-completion questionnaires are similar to those for self-completion questionnaires in general.

★   Those who complete them tend to be the most well educated and generally the higher income groups. Those who have difficulty reading, for whatever reason, are unlikely to respond.

★   The respondent must work within the structure of the questionnaire and so is limited in the response he/she can give. This is not too much of a problem if work has been done to check that the questions asked are those the respondent finds important (through interviews at an early stage and during piloting of the questionnaires) and also if space is allowed for comments.

★   The respondent is not allowed any participation in the decision making process – he/she cannot help by suggesting solutions to problems.

## The Interview Method

When using the interview method a larger area or number of issues can be covered in depth, but more time and expense will be expended. Given that interviews are very labour intensive, it is probably best to make as much use of the interview as possible and plan for it to last at least an hour and a half unless this would strain the physical or mental health of the respondent. Pilots will still be necessary, but an interview, particularly one with some unstructured questions ('Tell me about what happened when ...') allows for some explanation and interpretation of questions and responses.

The response rate is usually high if prospective interviewees are sent a letter prior to their being contacted by an interviewer, and if the interviewer is flexible about time, calling to make an appointment to interview if necessary.

The *advantages* of using the interview method are as follows.

★ It can collect a large amount of detailed information.

★ More people are likely to respond, including those with reading difficulties.

★ If unstructured as well as structured questions are used, it can collect explanatory information and can probe the reasons *why* certain courses of action have/have not been followed.

The *main disadvantage* of the interview method is that it is costly and labour intensive: large surveys of 400–500 respondents will require a team of trained interviewers, plus a supervisor or researcher to check questionnaires for systematic interviewer errors in order to eliminate them early, generally keep the standard of recording at a high level, and debrief interviewers about problems and emotional stress.

The survey is not the only approach which can be adopted in order to find out the views and needs of people who do not currently use health services. It is also possible to contact local community groups and voluntary organisations through the Community Health Council, and to work with these groups to investigate views. For example, meetings of residents living on a particular housing estate can be organised in urban areas, or with the help of Parish Councils, in rural areas. Purchasers will probably also want to contact GPs to find out their referral preferences.

A number of health authorities are establishing community links as a source of information. For example, Coventry Health Authority is using a King's Fund Centre development worker to help integrate quality measures into service contracts, and working with community groups as part of this process. An example of working with black and minority community groups in a similar context is described by Winn and Chotai (1990).

It is also possible to combine the survey and non-survey approaches – perhaps by surveying GPs, interviewing certain target groups of potential users, and working with community groups to establish the needs of other types of users. Again, the most effective approach is probably one using a number of methods.

The aim of this examination of the pre-coded questionnaire survey method is not to argue against its use, but to discourage use except in the appropriate circumstances and following expert planning and advice.

# Qualitative Methods

These methods involve the collection and analysis of narrative information. Generalisation and abbreviation still take place and so there is loss of information from the subject of study, but this reduction usually emerges from the information given rather than from the service provider. This is because the analysis of conversations and written information usually involves the worker looking for common patterns which emerge from the material, rather than imposing them upon the material from the beginning.

This does not mean that qualitative methods are automatically 'user-led'. An interview with a patient can be so highly structured by the interviewer that the response can be predetermined. This 'structuring' can be in the questions asked, the environment or the body language of the interviewer. For example, questions starting 'Do you think/feel ... ' can be leading, as in 'Do you think the nurses were helpful enough?' asked by a uniformed nurse with a dominant expression, in a small, bare white painted room, surrounded by syringes and other intimidating items of medical paraphernalia! Who would answer 'No' in this situation?

There are two different categories of methods to collect qualitative information. The first category consists of methods derived from the social science tradition: questionnaires, interviews, discussion groups, participant observation and diary keeping. The second category consists of informal (or 'quasi') methods adapted from many different sources: patient advocates, liaison officers, patients' councils, patients' forums, advisory groups and public meetings. Methods involving suggestion boxes, help lines and analysis of complaints are not described here but are covered in McIver and Carr-Hill (1989), and in the International Hospital Federation publication *And What Would They Know About It?* (1988). These formal and informal ('quasi') methods will now be examined in more detail.

## Self-completion Questionnaires

If open-ended questions are used in a questionnaire, then the information collected will be more 'user-led'. Such questions are of the kind which read 'What did you like least about ... ?' Unfortunately, this approach has two limitations: first, only those who can read and write will be able to respond; and secondly, the greater the number of people who fill in the questionnaire, the more time consuming it will be to analyse the responses, because each will have to be read individually and the patterns of answers noted (eg half of those answering this particular question mentioned the food, or whatever).

The first limitation can be overcome to a large extent by using the questionnaire as an interview schedule with those who cannot read or write, and with ethnic interpreters where the difficulty is due to inability to speak English. The second limitation does not have a solution, so most researchers limit the number of respondents to 100 or less at each session.

Having said this, those who are very interested in the responses and have set enough time aside for analysis can cope with slightly higher numbers of responses. An example is given in *The Health Service Journal*, 12 July 1990, p. 1035. Here Mark Learmonth in 'Please Speak Your Mind' describes how as the Outpatient Services Manager for York District Hospital, he sent out 193 letters requesting comments, enclosing paper and a pre-paid self-addressed envelope. He received 120 'unstructured' replies, but found the time consuming analysis worthwhile because for a cost of less than £100 he received information which helped him to 'understand more about people's perceptions of things such as doctors' attitudes, the atmosphere of the outpatient department and our car parking problems'.

Another way of using essentially the same method is to ask patients as they are leaving the outpatient department, or on discharge, just two questions:

★   What did you like most about your visit (or stay) ?

★   What did you like least about your visit (or stay) ?

This will produce information about the events which stand out in the user's mind, but it will not produce comments on all aspects of the service. If patients are notified before their consultation or stay in hospital that they will probably be asked these two questions, it will prepare them for it and allow them to start reflecting on their experiences, which may result in more information.

The key to using this type of open-ended questionnaire is to keep the numbers of respondents down to manageable proportions because a great mass of replies will be very confusing to analyse. If large numbers of responses are required it is best to either break the number into batches and analyse the responses of the first batch before tackling the second; or use the unstructured questionnaire as a way of finding out a recurring pattern of important issues and then construct a structured (pre-coded/categorised) questionnaire from these issues to distribute to a larger number of people.

## Interviews

There are three different kinds of interview: structured, semi-structured and open. These terms relate to the degree to which questions are set by the interviewer. In *structured* interviews all questions are listed by the interviewer and are asked in a set order. In *semi-structured* interviews some questions are set and some left open. In an *open* interview no questions are formally set. The term 'open' means that topics are brought up for general discussion and these topics can be determined by the person being interviewed.

For example, a structured interview about a person's stay in hospital may include a number of questions about specific topics. The responses will differ from those given in response to a questionnaire only in that they will contain more detailed information – the interviewer can ask for more explanation where he/she does not understand. In a semi-structured interview some of the questions will be set, but others will require the interviewer to bring up a topic and discuss it. An open interview is closest to a discussion or conversation. The interviewer will gently direct the conversation in the direction needed to gain the most useful information, though not 'leading' the person being interviewed by suggesting what the interviewer would like to hear.

Interviewing is a skilled job, and the open interview in particular requires very experienced personnel – it is closer to counselling than to market research interviewing.

Critical incident technique (CIT) is another approach which is directed at collecting information about what happened to a person and about what they liked or disliked about their experiences. The method has been very fully described and its use illustrated in the North West Thames Regional Health Authority / Industrial Training Research Unit publication *Managing Customer Relations* (1986).

CIT seems to be gaining support as a method and has recently been used by a number of health organisations, including the Scottish Health Service Management Development Group, Mid-Glamorgan Health Authority and Oxfordshire Health Authority. Michael Pryce-Jones, the management consultant used by Oxford Regional Health Authority to develop use of the technique in the region, has written a number of articles on the subject (see 'Not How Many But Why: A Qualitative Approach to Customer Relations', *Health Service Management*, December 1988, pp. 175–177, and 'Satisfactory Practice', *The Health Service Journal*, 30 November 1989, pp. 1464–5).

## Discussion Groups

Many people are not articulate and so are not able to respond well in interviews. They may feel more relaxed, however, amongst people who have gone through similar experiences. Also, as part of a group they may find their experiences given shape and form in the words of others, and so be better able to express their own views.

The method is not yet widely used within health authorities but it is regularly used by market research companies, where it is commonly known as the group depth interview, focus group or focused group discussion. In the USA, where it has been used extensively since the 1950s, the number of group interview projects commissioned each year far exceeds the number of surveys (Goldman and McDonald, 1987).

In Britain the discussion group has been used extensively by Social and Community Planning Research (SCPR), an organisation which also runs training workshops on research methods, including the discussion group. The SCPR publication *Keeping in Touch with the Talking: The Community Care Needs of People with a Mental Illness* (1988) gives details of use of this method during a research study carried out on behalf of the Birmingham Community Care Special Action Project.

One or two health authorities are beginning to use the method. For example, East Birmingham Hospital ran a discussion group session with patients attending a pain clinic in the outpatient department in July 1990. Members of East Birmingham and Solihull Community Health Councils ran the discussion, which was organised by the outpatient services manager.

## Observation

Observation can be either qualitative or quantitative. It is possible to have a number of predetermined events written down and simply tick a box every time each event occurs. It is also possible to write down what is observed in a narrative form, or to video record these events.

Both of these methods are useful, particularly when interviews or questionnaires may be too disruptive (eg in A & E departments) or where *events* are more important than opinions or experiences. In some instances personal experience may be difficult to relate owing to traumatic circumstances or because actions are performed unconsciously (eg working habits can be 'automatic' and so below the level of conscious awareness), and then it is more useful to watch and record.

An extension of this technique is that of participant observation, which is similar to 'shadowing'. The aim here is to obtain some experience of what it feels like to be involved in a particular activity. For example, it may be useful to stay with a patient throughout their visit to hospital, although this is more likely to be feasible with patients attending clinics, outpatient departments or A & E than with inpatients. Patients or clients may, however, object to being observed in some situations: for example, clients in a study by Atkinson (1985) were happy to be observed at home but not outside it.

The problem with this method is that information produced relates only to one individual experience, so it is useful mainly as an aid to understanding the kinds of issues that are likely to be important to the patient. Nevertheless, if two individuals repeated the experience twice weekly, after a period of time it would be possible to make generalisations. When using this technique it is important to make notes at frequent intervals, otherwise details of the experience will be quickly forgotten.

## Keeping a Diary

Some individuals can be encouraged to keep a diary of 'what happens to them during their visit to hospital' and this can produce useful information, particularly if they are encouraged to record their thoughts and feelings as well as the events which happen to them. Obviously only those who can write would be able to take part in this approach, and the end result would vary considerably in comprehensiveness and clarity between different individuals, so limiting usefulness. Nevertheless, Atkinson (1985) used this method successfully with people who had learning difficulties, which implies that it is more useful than might at first appear.

It is likely that the number of individuals who would be willing or able to take part in this activity would be small and so it would be best used in conjunction with other methods if generalisations are to be made. Atkinson used it in conjunction with a study of case notes, focused interviews with social workers, interviews with clients and participant observation. Diaries were used in conjunction with group discussions by Newcastle Inner City Forum and Newcastle Community Health Council during a project on women's health during the period 1981–83.

## Patient Advocates

Advocacy is rapidly becoming a widely used word in the NHS. At its simplest level to advocate is to plead on behalf of another, but this basic concept has developed in a number of ways. Robson (1987) has defined advocacy as 'the realisation of a person's interests' and has identified three different models:

★ **Lay or citizens' advocacy** – where skilled *volunteers* supported by an independent agency work with individuals on a long term basis

★ **Paid advocacy** – where skilled workers are paid by an independent agency to represent the interests of individuals, usually in the short term

★ **Self-advocacy** – where, singularly or collectively, individuals work on their own behalf to realise their own interests.

At present these different types of advocacy usually involve vulnerable groups, such as people with learning difficulties or mental health problems, elderly people, and black and minority groups.

The Advocacy Alliance was the first example of a *citizens' advocacy* project in Britain. This was funded by the DHSS and its method was to develop relationships between volunteer advocates and long-stay hospital residents with learning difficulties. The advocates helped the residents in ways such as

managing their money or securing them places in the
community that matched their expectations and needs (Sang
and O'Brien, 1984). Advice on setting up a citizens' advocacy
project based upon experiences gained with a citizens' advocacy
office for people with learning difficulties is given by Butler and
Forrest (1990). A scheme for the elderly is currently being run by
Camden Age Concern. This is called 'Voice', and it 'links
volunteer advocates to elderly people when they are making
major decisions which will affect the rest of their lives or are
facing change over which they have little control' (Age Concern,
1989).

The Multi-Ethnic Women's Project in Hackney is an example of
*paid advocacy*. Workers are paid to support black and minority
women using the maternity services. The workers translate for
the women and help to ensure that they receive treatment which
meets their cultural expectations (Cornwell and Gordon, 1984).
Another common form of paid advocacy is found in projects
such as the Advice and Legal Representation Project at
Springfield Psychiatric Hospital, which provides legal advice
and representation to patients and staff (Robson, 1987).

An example of *self-advocacy* is the organisation People First,
which helps people with learning difficulties to participate in
the development of services by giving them confidence and
skills to take part in meetings (Whittaker, 1990). Details of a
number of mental health self-advocacy groups and information
about this area of self-advocacy can be found in Campbell (1990).

## Liaison Officer

Strictly speaking a patient advocate, whether paid, voluntary or
there to facilitate self-advocacy, should work on behalf of the
client rather than merely convey his or her views, but the
principle can be loosened to apply to any workers who act as
'go-betweens' representing the views of the patient to the health
service providers and those of the service providers to the
patient.

The advocacy movement may not be in favour of this loosening, in that it can be seen as a weakening of the principle of empowering users; but it is better to make a step in the direction of better communication with and improved information from service users by the use of a liaison officer or 'go-between' than to make no step at all. The employment of a liaison officer can be a necessary intermediary stage between a provider-led service and one in which users are working with advocates who empower them to have a greater say in service provision.

Liaison workers are particularly important where the patient group is disadvantaged or in a position of little power, or where the language and culture of birth of group members is not English; but it can improve the chances of obtaining accurate information about patient views in most cases. A liaison officer is more likely to be seen as independent than health care staff, yet will have the status of a 'permanent' worker that researchers do not usually have. Sometimes patients can feel that researchers 'will not understand because this is just another project to them'.

A liaison officer or worker will have the time to build up expertise as well as develop a trusting relationship with long-stay patients or regular visitors. They will also have time to develop relationships with staff and relevant community groups, so increasing their ability to present a clear picture of the strengths and weaknesses of a service, and to convey information between the different groups involved.

## Patients' Council

Patients' Councils constitute one of two main ways that self-advocacy is developing in the mental health services in Britain. The idea originated in the early 1970s following complaints by some service users about the quality of their mental health services (Gell, 1990). A person who is or has been a user of mental health services acts as a facilitator so as to gain the trust and participation of patients on the ward. Staff are excluded from meetings where patients put forward their complaints about current services and make suggestions about future services. The facilitator takes these views to the management for discussion.

Nottingham Patients' Council was the first to be organised in Britain and is now funded by Nottingham Patients' Council Support Group, an organisation which also provides advice and information about this model of patient advocacy. Andrew Lowe, in an information pack supplied by Nottingham Patients' Council Support Group (NPCSG), describes the approach of patients' councils as 'neither a confrontational nor a consensus approach, but a negotiable approach. Propositions and complaints are modified or resolved through a series of negotiations, first at ward or unit level and where that is not possible, via the bi-monthly hospital Council'. For further information on NPCSG, see also Gell (1990).

## Health Forum

The mental health forum is the second of the two main ways that self-advocacy is developing in the mental health services. Forums now exist in Lambeth and Bromley, and take the form of an umbrella organisation, within the context of which all interested parties can become involved in planning local mental health services. Those involved include the voluntary sector, users, carers and health professionals. Bromley Mental Health Forum began in 1987 and in the first 20 months it held five general meetings with an average attendance of about 100 people (Jones, 1989).

A similar kind of health forum, but of a more general nature – 'a forum where local people can contribute their views on health needs and healthcare planning' – was recommended by the report of the Community Nursing Review in 1986 (the Cumberlege Report) as necessary 'if health authorities and health professionals are to take the interests of the consumer seriously' (HMSO, 1986). Merton and Sutton Health Authority provides an example of an organisation which has implemented this recommendation in Carshalton. The Carshalton Healthcare Association held its first meeting in April 1989 and invited workers in statutory and voluntary agencies, carers, the private sector and local NHS users (Roberts and Lee, 1990).

## Advisory Groups

This term covers a wide range of groups of different kinds set up to advise health professionals on the views of users. They may have an all professional membership, an all consumer membership, or be made up of a mixture of professionals and consumers. The role of these groups can vary from gathering and presenting the views of users, to discussing and making decisions about service provision.

For example, the Outpatient Department at Harold Wood Hospital, Barking, Havering and Brentwood Health Authority, has a Patient Users' Group which has been running since January 1989. This is an advisory group comprising service users and representatives from voluntary and self-help organisations who meet once a month on average. Their role is to provide professionals with information about the views and needs of service users. This has included suggestions about improvements to the waiting environment, provision of patient information and a review of internal and external signposting.

Another example is the local Community Advisory Group set up by Darlington Health Authority. This grew out of work carried out by the Community Unit in conjunction with an organisation called Cultural Partnerships Ltd (see Useful Addresses section, p. 95) in 1987. Three health festivals led to the setting up of the group, which comprises 21 members including local lay people and professionals.

Advisory groups can meet with difficulties arising out of ambiguities over their role and status, and also as a result of the mixed membership of the group. A case study and advice can be found in Winn and Quick (1989).

## Public Meetings/User Consultation Days

Although valuable, public meetings can be a stressful way to obtain user views: first, it is not possible to tell in advance how many people will turn up; and secondly, if one or two individuals with forceful views are present, it may be difficult to balance the meeting and allow enough people to express their views. These two problems can be overcome to some extent by inviting named individuals, as well as advertising locally, and by structuring the day so that views are obtained in a workshop atmosphere.

For example, the Mental Health Unit at Newcastle Health Authority used HSTA Management Consultants (see Useful Addresses section, p. 95) to arrange a public consultation day in 1986. The audience was invited and consisted of voluntary bodies, individuals and community organisations. Posters advertising the day were put up in local shops, libraries etc. Out of the 120 individuals and organisations circulated, 60 people attended, all from the invited list, but a 50/50 professional/lay person split was achieved. A workshop format was followed, with those present being split into seven groups. There were two sessions, the first tackling the needs and problems of elderly people with a mental illness and their carers; and the second suggestions for improvements to existing services or new services. These were followed by a panel discussion and a 'market place' exercise where people had the opportunity to put ticks by statements on large sheets of paper on the wall. A wealth of useful information was collected and a five part plan drawn up.

This type of exercise probably works best if it is focused on a specific service or client group, or takes place within an easily identifiable community. This is because people need to be very motivated to attend and if a specific issue is addressed, those likely to be concerned can be invited.

Health service providers have a wide range of methods to choose from to obtain the views of users of their services. Each method has advantages and disadvantages, and – particularly where the informal or quasi-methods are concerned – these can often only be learned from experience. This makes the exchange of information about the use of these methods a particularly important activity.

## Method Related Questions to Ask Before Starting a Feedback Exercise

★ Do you need quantitative answers or qualitative ones? (How many? or What?/Why?)

★ Have you read what others have done in this area? Does this answer your question or do you need further information? What lessons can you learn from previous approaches?

★ Do you have skilled personnel to carry out research tasks such as interviewing, survey design and analysis and report writing?

★ How much time, money, manpower and other resources do you have?

★ Have you planned and costed each stage of the exercise? (ie setting up, information gathering, analysis and report writing)

★ What alternative methods could you use, and how would they compare in terms of cost and probable information outcome? Is the method you have chosen definitely the best for your purposes?

★ Is there management commitment to make changes in the direction indicated by the feedback exercise?

# 5 ANALYSIS OF DATA

The process of analysis involves making sense of the information collected. That is, it is a process of drawing out patterns and construing meaning. This process will differ depending on whether the data are of a quantitative or qualitative kind, and it will be informed by the objectives and aims of the exercise. It is useful to look at these two variables in more detail.

## Qualitative and Quantitative Data Analysis

Analysis is closely connected to the whole process of data collection. Where a *quantitative* method such as a structured questionnaire is used, it is clear that responses to questions should be recorded and these form the items of data to be analysed. Analysis in this case will often consist of little more than aggregating the scores. That is, counting the numbers of people who tick a 'yes' (or 'very satisfactory') box in answer to a question, then going through the same procedure for those ticking 'no', and so on through the questions. The whole process is often carried out using a computer program designed for the task.

Although the procedure is simple, this does not mean that anyone can carry out the analysis. Expertise will be needed to draw inferences from the statistics. The fact that 60 per cent of people ticked the 'yes' box in answer to a question needs interpretation by someone who can relate the scores to any obtained in similar exercises carried out previously, either by the same organisation or elsewhere. Furthermore he or she must understand the limitations of the questions asked and those of the sample of respondents. He or she must have a good knowledge of the research aims and of what will be important to those whose job it is to read the final report and act on the recommendations.

Having said this, the procedure for collecting and analysing data *appears* far simpler in the case of quantitative methods (such as questionnaire surveys) than for qualitative methods (such as discussion groups or open interviews) or 'quasi-methods' (such as advisory groups and patient advocates). For instance, it is not at all obvious what should be recorded during discussion groups or health forums. This is perhaps why the survey is so popular with health service providers: social science expertise is not usually available 'in-house' and it is expensive to employ specialists. An apparently simpler method is an advantage.

It can be argued, however, that this simplicity is deceptive and that this is one of the reasons why the results of many surveys prove to be so disappointing to the inexperienced health service staff who undertake them. Apart from the many mistakes that can be made at the design stage of the exercise, statistics derived from structured questions are *not* simple to interpret and this is one reason why the results are often difficult to act upon.

As far as qualitative social science methods (such as discussion groups) are concerned, rules of procedure have been laid down. Informal or quasi-methods (such as health forums) are different, but it can be argued that the same basic principles apply.

In order to understand what these basic principles are, it is worth considering again what is meant by the term 'accurate'. The method used must collect information which is accurate.

That is, information which is a true reflection of what service users experience, think or feel, or of how they behave.

The technical terms relating to accuracy are 'validity' and 'reliability'. Some social scientists have argued that quantitative research is high on reliability and low on validity while the reverse is true of qualitative research (Filstead, 1970). Others have argued that by following rigorous, systematic and transparent approaches to qualitative research, reliability can be improved (Walker, 1985). A combination of both types of method will certainly help to overcome the limitations of each used alone.

To assess the nature of these limitations, particularly as applied to qualitative research (which is often thought to be the less scientific and more complicated of the two), it is necessary to examine the terms 'validity' and 'reliability' is more detail.

## Validity

Walker (1985) identifies four aspects of validity: descriptive, conceptual, theoretical and external.

★ **Descriptive validity** – This relates to whether incidents, acts or statements were recorded correctly. That is, were they described or otherwise noted without distortions or omissions? It also involves a level one step removed from the collection of data to its interpretation: is the meaning being given to it by the person who has analysed the information an appropriate one or not?

★ **Conceptual validity** – This refers to the analysis in a more direct sense. That is, where categorisation and similar summaries of the information under headings are presented, does the content match the description of the category. Are the categories really distinct and different or do they merge together? Where do the categories come from – the writer or the respondent?

★ **Theoretical validity** – This deals with the way the concepts fit together to form a theory. Where research is not directly linked into a discipline such as social science, the term 'theory' will probably refer to 'argument' or 'recommendations'. That is, does the evidence support the argument?

★ **External validity** – This concerns the generalisability of the theory (or recommendations). It applies most notably to the question of whether information about user views collected for one particular service in one area of the country also holds for users of other services or the same service elsewhere. This will depend upon the nature of the sample drawn upon and in qualitative research this is unlikely to be a statistically representative one. The important questions therefore are whether the respondents are typical of people in this category (eg users of maternity services) and whether they are typical of users of all health services.

Validity, then, has to do with how closely the information collected represents a slice of 'reality'. That is, the world outside the researcher's world. This is not the place to get into a discussion about objectivity and subjectivity or whether 'facts' exist independently of human concepts. The issue here is over the relative merits of qualitative or quantitative data collection methods with regard to validity.

Qualitative methods collect information which is likely to be more valid because analysis is 'bottom up' rather than 'top down'. That is, concepts arise from the information, whereas in the analysis of quantitative data, the concepts are pre-existing. For example, in structured questionnaires the questions and responses are fixed in advance, which means that the respondent has to make his or her reply fit a pre-existing category. This may not be a true reflection of that person's view on a particular issue.

## Reliability

Reliability, on the other hand, is about repeatability. That is, whether the findings would be reproduced if the whole exercise were carried out again. It is generally true that the more variables there are, the less likely it is that the same event will occur or can be made to occur again. Qualitative methods collect complex information which involves lots of variables. Quantitative methods, on the other hand, simplify by pre-categorisation and standardisation. The variables are controlled by limiting the responses and controlling the way the information is collected. This means that the same results can be achieved again.

Returning to the basic principles of collecting and analysing information, it is clear that in order to be accurate information must:

★ be based upon authentic descriptions of acts, observations or statements

★ be analysed in a way which shows the direct and justified relationship between these descriptions and the categories they are put into

★ make clear the relationship between these categories and the recommendations made

★ be specific about how generalisable these recommendations are.

Those using quasi-methods should try to adhere to these basic principles as closely as possible. For example, during meetings of advisory groups or health forums the aim should be to try and record as much as possible, particularly in the early stages when it is not clear what will emerge as important and what will turn out to be a passing comment.

When one person is managing a session and it involves considerable dialogue, it is usually best to tape record the proceedings. This will enable the group facilitator to relax a little and follow the conversation, encouraging it to proceed along useful lines. Alternatively, if two people are involved, one can pay attention to the structure of the discussion and manage proceedings while the other notes particularly interesting points and jots down indicators of who is speaking, to help when the tape is transcribed. This is a useful back up to the tape, which can become inaudible when two or three people speak at once or someone moves noisily at a critical moment.

Complete transcription of dialogue from tape to paper is extremely time consuming: probably 4–5 hours for a one and a half hour discussion. It is very useful to have complete transcripts, but if *what* is being said is more important than *how*, *when* or *by whom* it is said, then it is possible to obtain a satisfactory amount of data by listening to the tape and summarising what it said. A number of typical sentences and sections of dialogue can be transcribed as verbatim quotes for illustration purposes.

The aim of data collection is to record as much information as possible as it occurs and not have to rely on memory. The memory records information in a biased and unsystematic way, and although you might believe it will retain the important points, it is not always possible to know initially what is and is not important because this may only emerge later as issues recur.

Having said this, it is still important to note down your own perceptions of what seems important as these can be useful in making sense of the material when you start analysis; but these observations should be kept separate.

# Collation of Data

Before the data can be analysed, they need to be broken down and collated into manageable chunks. Again, this is a relatively easy process where questionnaires are concerned because the chunks can be the different sections of the questionnaire, but what is a manageable chunk if a discussion group has been used to collect information? Is it one session or a series of sessions taken together and collated under different topics? What about the data produced by a liaison officer?

Usually, with discussion groups, it is a series of discussion groups tackling a particular issue which is equivalent to the survey and the issues that emerge around the questions asked are the 'responses' or 'chunks'.

An advisory group meeting is slightly different and it is probably best to try and collate information after each session of this kind of group meeting. Whether a full report is written after each meeting will depend upon the number of points raised, but given the amount of time needed to produce a full report it is likely that information from a number of sessions will need to be recorded, collated and analysed before a report is prepared.

A liaison officer should make notes during and immediately after each meeting with service users and others who give information about service use. He/she should collate the information frequently (probably once a week) and collect it into a report at regular intervals (perhaps every three months).

The collation process involves relating the information gathered to information which has been collated by others doing similar kinds of work, in order to set it in context and aid in the understanding and location of important points.

# Analysis of Data

Analysis is the process of making sense of the data collected. Many people find it useful to draw up tables categorising the data, or construct grids, flow charts or maps with it. This enables them to examine the relationship between different aspects of the information collected.

Certainly it is worth following a step by step procedure, such as:

★ summarising the material into a series of points

★ looking for recurring points and noting how many times they occur and with what qualifications or differences, if any

★ aggregating the information by noting the most frequently occurring points and any other points which seem to be of particular importance, bearing in mind the context.

At this stage it is sometimes worth writing up the 'findings' and offering them to the original discussion group or forum for comments, particularly if some points are unclear. These 'findings' will then go towards the production of a draft report.

# Analysis, Research Objective and Aim

The objectives of the research will influence the way in which the information collected is analysed. By research *objective* is meant the reason a particular method is being used, rather than the overall purpose for which the information will be used, which is the *aim* of the research.

For example, a research objective might be to explore an issue using a qualitative method, with the aim of producing an instrument to use to collect quantitative information for the monitoring of standards. This objective will influence analysis because it will direct the mind of the person doing it in a particular direction – in this case the analysis will be looking for issues that respondents consider important and for typical sentences which express views on these issues.

The aim of the exercise to collect user views will also influence the analysis because the person doing the analysis will be anxious to answer the questions posed at the outset. Sometimes the pressure to answer questions, or to answer them in a particular way, can be so great that validity is compromised. With qualitative research this is most likely to take place at the analysis stage, rather than during design as can often happen in quantitative research.

A large structured survey can produce figures which are reliable but information which is not necessarily valid, so that too much *interpretation* is placed upon the results; while a few unstructured interviews can produce valid information which is not necessarily generalisable, so that too much *weight* is given to the results.

This kind of distortion is less likely to take place if those organising the user feedback project are clear at the outset about what it is intended to achieve.

# 6 DISSEMINATION OF RESULTS

If the only people who hear about the consumer feedback project are the researcher and staff who are immediately involved in it, then the findings will have little effect. A report which goes directly onto a shelf where it lies gathering dust is a waste of time, money and effort.

The dissemination of results starts at the planning stage of the project. Not only should sufficient time, money and expertise for dissemination be built into the project from the beginning, but also members of the prospective audience for the results can be usefully alerted in advance to arouse interest and allow them to make it part of their future agenda.

The final detail of how the results of a consumer feedback project are disseminated will depend upon the aim of the exercise, whether this involves monitoring, evaluation etc. However, a number of general points can be made. The process can be spilt into two main aspects, which are related: these are the *way* in which results are presented (the medium); and *who* they are presented to (the audience).

# The Medium

Whichever medium is eventually chosen to disseminate results it is important that an initial report is written, and this should be as comprehensive as possible. Distortions and omissions can easily occur if summaries are written from the raw data too early on. A comprehensive report forms a foundation which can be returned to for clarification or elaboration if later interpretations are challenged.

It is useful if the comprehensive report includes the following sections.

I   **Introduction** – Background to the study, sometimes including a brief literature review of the area.

II   **Method** – A descriptive section on how the information was collected, number of people interviewed or otherwise asked for information, number of people who were asked to take part but refused etc.

III   **Results** – The information collected, often using direct quotes to illustrate points.

IV   **Discussion and Conclusion** – Any qualifications or additional information obtained from other sources which might reflect upon the results is discussed before conclusions are drawn up.

V   **Recommendations** – These are suggestions for changes, based on the information collected during the study. They are sometimes attached to the report at the beginning rather than the end.

VI   **Appendices** – These should include any questionnaires or interview schedules used, and also some assessment of the exercise itself. Were there problems with the method used? How were these overcome, if at all? Should changes in the procedure be made in future? This section will be valuable to others who are about to attempt something similar, as well as being part of a learning process for those involved.

Once the comprehensive report has been written, various summaries and fact sheets can be compiled, drawing out important parts for different audiences. These can be pinned to notice boards, form part of displays, be transferred to slides for presentations, form newsflashes for 'in-house' and local newspapers etc. In sum, the findings can be presented in ways which make them accessible to targeted audiences.

Determination as well as imagination is important at this stage and it is probably better to get others involved besides the original researchers or staff because they may well be hesitant about 'broadcasting' their work. In any case, different skills are involved.

# The Audience

There are a number of important audiences for the results of user feedback work, and different types of presentation may suit each. For example:

★ **Health service managers, professionals and staff**
   *Possible media:* Reports and presentations to working groups etc; seminars involving different groups of staff with an interest or involvement in the service concerned; in-house journal; staff training courses and events.

★ **Informed lay people** – such as health authority members, CHC members, those involved in voluntary groups, pressure groups, black and minority groups and community organisations
   *Possible media:* Reports and presentations; fact sheets.

★ **Service users who took part in the survey/exercise** – or whose
  relatives and friends might have done so
  *Possible media:* Display boards at relevant sites, such as
  waiting areas of service departments, wards, day rooms,
  entrance lobbies etc.

★ **Other service users and the local community in general**
  *Possible media:* Local newspaper, radio, health newspaper,
  open days etc.

★ **Other health authorities and customer feedback officers**
  *Possible media:* The King's Fund Consumer Feedback
  Resource; Health Service Journal, professional journals etc.

Poor dissemination of results occurs in all areas of health service
research, not just that involving consumer feedback, or that
which is conducted 'in-house'. In an article addressing the issue,
Russell, Hunter and Macpherson (1990) ask whether
dissemination of health services research findings merits more
effort than is usual in other fields of medical research. Their
answer is 'an unequivocal yes'.

> ... partly because of the need to discuss the likely influence of local
> variations on successful policy implementation and practice, and
> partly because the kind of professional network of researchers–
> cum–practitioners that exists for biomedical research has not yet
> been developed for health services research.  (p. 94)

In the field of consumer feedback about health services,
methodological advances would be more likely if those involved
'in-house' kept in touch with one another and with academic
researchers engaged in similar work. The King's Fund
Consumer Feedback Resource is keen to facilitate this process
and welcomes details of projects and contact names.

The issue that particularly concerns Russell, Hunter and Macpherson, however, involves a second question – that of how best to disseminate research findings so that they can have a more widespread influence on services, or at least on planning for services. Drawing on Paine and Bellamy (1982), they describe three broad purposes of dissemination:

★ to share information

★ to generate support for a new approach

★ to assist a service agency in adopting and implementing an innovative practice.

These three purposes require the dissemination of different types of material in different ways. Raising awareness about issues (eg describing users' experiences and views about a particular service) can be distinguished from campaigning for a new approach to getting user feedback (eg critical incident technique), and these in turn can be separated from helping staff to change the way they deliver a service.

The latter exercise is particularly difficult and Russell and co-workers comment:

> … for change to result from research, the local climate has to be favourable and the research findings have to meet a locally perceived need for information, or address an explicit local question. If the particular service is not at this stage of evolution, local seminars are unlikely to stimulate immediate change. (p. 95)

While this comment probably applies to the dissemination of good practice across different districts or units rather than within a particular unit, it may apply to different disciplines or services within one unit, and those wishing to encourage a multi-disciplinary approach to tackling service improvement should bear it in mind.

The process of disseminating information about user views to staff involved in service provision also requires considerable skill. At the very least it demands careful planning with attention to how, when and in what way the information is conveyed. Ideally, those involved will have had some training in group facilitation or counselling, and will understand how to convey information which could be construed as criticism in a supportive environment which allows the expression of anger and frustration, without letting it get out of hand and affect morale. Those involved should also know how to ensure that change is implemented and maintained.

# 7 PLANNING CONSUMER FEEDBACK ACTIVITIES

The planning stage is a critical one if the aim of collecting accurate and useful information about user views is to be achieved. Planning takes place at two main levels: the planning of a programme of activities to collect user views; and the planning of individual projects.

## A Consumer Feedback Programme

If consumer feedback is to be used effectively, managers are advised to plan with the following aims in mind.

### Aims

★ that user feedback becomes an integrated part of other activities and not a 'bolt on extra'

★ that feedback activities persist over time and are not considered to be 'one-off' exercises

★ that a body of knowledge about user experiences and views develops and is used to inform and train staff

★   that changes to services take place in response to user
feedback, and that these changes are evaluated to see
whether quality of service has improved from the user
perspective.

A planned programme will contribute towards the achievement
of these aims because it will ensure that a systematic approach is
taken. The programme should probably include the following
objectives.

## Objectives

★   Be as *comprehensive* as possible.

That is, it should aim to address all service areas and assess
how much is known about user views; whether problems
in service delivery have already been identified and what
kinds of activities most require consumer information
(planning, evaluation, monitoring of standards etc).

★   *Prioritise* areas for feedback projects, so that resources can
be used effectively.

This will probably be linked to wider quality initiatives and
will include basic approaches to gathering information
from users and staff, such as suggestion boxes.

★   Give some consideration to *methodological* issues.

That is, what expertise exists 'in-house', whether good
contacts exist with outside research agencies, how expertise
can be developed.

★   Consider the issue of an *information database*.

Containing the results of feedback work, health needs,
other sources of similar information etc.

★   Discuss *staff training and education* following feedback work
and on customer related issues in general.

The management structure implied by such a programme could include the following elements.

★   *Senior management promotion* of the programme and commitment to a total quality approach which recognises the importance of the service user, both internal and external.

★   *Staff ownership* of the programme through their involvement in particular aspects of it. Even though prioritisation has taken place, all staff can be encouraged to think of how services might be improved from the customer's point of view.

★   *A user feedback working party or committee*, preferably multi-disciplinary, which is able to oversee the planning, prioritisation, timetabling and costing of the programme and individual projects, to assess results and monitor action.

★   *A consumer feedback officer*, to take responsibility for co-ordinating projects, obtaining and collating information to help individual projects, giving advice on methods; monitoring timetables and overseeing the writing of reports and the dissemination of information. This person can also liaise with external researchers if these are employed to carry out projects. The facilitating and liaising role is an extremely important one although this person should not feel that they are solely responsible for the success of projects.

★   *Project working groups* of staff involved in particular feedback activities. These can handle the details of individual projects, and will probably be productively involved at the early stage of providing details about what user feedback information already exists in a particular service area and what needs to be done. Without this level of organisation, projects are unlikely to have staff ownership and the process of feeding information back to staff to ensure service change could be difficult. Even so, the relationship between the project working party and other staff in the service area is important and members of it will have to work hard to make sure other staff feel that their contributions are vital and that the working party is not taking all the responsibility for customer feedback and service improvement.

It is likely that a consumer feedback programme will be the responsibility of service providers and will inform service contract specifications, but purchasers will probably want to satisfy themselves that they agree on aims and that issues such as those covered in the list of objectives (comprehensiveness, prioritisation, methods, information and training) have been addressed. They may also want to know the kind of management structure which supports the process of obtaining user views.

# The Consumer Feedback Project

There are five main stages involved in each project. These are:

**1** Setting up the project

**2** Collecting the data

**3** Coding and analysing the data

**4** Writing the report

**5** Disseminating the results.

In theory these stages should be timetabled and costed before one begins, but in practice the first stage of setting up the project predates the timetabling. This is because a realistic timetable cannot be drawn up without some knowledge of what method will be used to collect customer views and this in turn will depend upon the answers to further questions, as earlier chapters have shown.

The following steps are involved in *setting up* a feedback project or activity.

**1** Establish the main aim and any subsidiary aims (keep these to a minimum) – See Chapter 3.

**2** Be clear about the questions that need to be answered – See Chapter 3.

**3** Consider the categories of customer involved – See Chapter 2.

**4** Do a literature/activity search to find out what has been done before: contact the King's Fund Centre Library or Consumer Feedback Resource, a local database or 'in-house' expert; or employ an organisation/consultant to do the work. (Subsequent stages are carried out in conjunction with the outside agency if this option is taken.)

**5** After considering the results of previous work, the aim, the types of customer involved and the budget available, decide on the method – See Chapter 4.

**6** Present an outline of the aim and method to the Ethical Committee, if necessary.

**7** Draw up a project timetable with the help of staff who are involved or whose work will be affected by it.

**8** Allocate tasks to staff and any others involved.

There are a number of books which give advice on how long the various stages of a user feedback project are likely to take (see Morton-Williams (1985) for projects involving qualitative methods such as interviews and discussion groups; and Dixon and Carr-Hill (1989) for surveys).

Obtaining the views of service users is not an easy activity, but once the basic principles are grasped, it is a straightforward one which rests upon a series of stages. Health service providers who decide to conduct consumer feedback activities 'in-house' will find that it *is* possible to develop expertise, and this booklet should help them to get started. They may need extra help with some projects – large surveys, for example, or the setting up and running of group discussions or patient advocacy schemes. They may also need help in training staff to understand and act upon results, if training and development workers are not available. Progress is possible however, even using such simple quasi-methods as suggestion boxes and patient liaison officers.

Those who decide to employ outside agencies after reading this book should by now understand the kind of expertise they need and know what to look for in proposals and research timetables.

# 8 CHECKLIST OF QUESTIONS TO ASK BEFORE STARTING

## Do you have the support of senior management ?

Without management commitment to making changes suggested by feedback from service users, you are likely to find yourself in a frustrating position at the end of all your hard work: the results and any recommendations made will lie gathering dust on a shelf. This will be a waste of your time and may cause disillusion amongst service users whose expectations for a better service have been raised by the process of obtaining their views. Make sure that senior management are interested in hearing the views of users and ready to make any necessary changes, or to include these in future plans.

## Is your consumer feedback work part of a larger programme to develop a consumer perspective ?

Although better than nothing, obtaining consumer views in a piecemeal fashion is not the most effective and efficient way for a health authority to become more responsive to service users. This is because change in one service area is likely to have implications for other services. Also, service users tend not to make distinctions between different services. Where feedback exercises are haphazard, there is a strong possibility that some services will be overlooked. A co-ordinated and planned programme for obtaining user views and making changes ensures the systematic tailoring of services to consumer needs and expectations.

## Are you clear about the purpose of the project ?

The views of consumers can be sought for a number of reasons. You may be about to make service changes anyway and want to know how best to present these changes to service users; you may want to evaluate the effectiveness of a change that has taken place; you may want to plan a new service, or review an old one; or you may want to monitor the day to day progress of a service. Different types of information are necessary in order to answer these different requirements and it is usually unwise to try and make one exercise serve a number of different purposes, unless the questions you want to ask are identical for each purpose or overlap considerably. For example, there is no point in collecting information about the kind of change service users prefer, if the changes are already taking place and what you really want to know is how to 'fine tune' these changes so that they are more 'user friendly'.

## Have you collected as much available information on the subject area as possible ?

If you have not checked what information has already been collected by your health authority, you might find yourself asking questions that have already been answered. If information already exists it is best to build upon it – in fact you may find that it alters the questions you want to ask. It also helps to know what other health authorities have found when conducting similar exercises. Sometimes enough evidence exists about user preferences to conduct a much smaller scale investigation than originally planned, or even to just go ahead and improve services in the way other studies have indicated is desirable from the consumers' point of view.

## What kind of information do you need ?

The choice of method you will use to collect information is partially dependent on the type of information you need. Some methods collect numerical information (statistics) and others collect narrative type information (explanatory and descriptive). Do you want information about percentages of people, or do you want to find out why a service is being used in a particular way, or about the opinions and experiences of users? Some methods are able to collect both types of information. Methods used to obtain statistical information are limited response questionnaire surveys and coded observation, whereas discussion groups and open-ended questionnaires or interview surveys collect narrative or explanatory information. You may want users to help you make decisions during service review or planning, and this will require user participation through forums and advisory groups.

## What type of customer is to supply the information you need ?

It is useful to categorise service users in order to help identify any methodological stumbling blocks that might arise. For example, it is no use handing out self-completion questionnaires if the majority of those who will complete them are elderly. Many elderly people have difficulty holding pens because of arthritis, and many have impaired sight and forget to carry their reading glasses with them. Also, some elderly people easily become confused by official forms. Your response rate is likely to be poor unless you use the questionnaire as an interview schedule. Other categories, such as ethnic minorities, may have difficulty reading English.

## Have you considered a wide range of methods for obtaining feedback ?

It is a mistake to think automatically that a patient satisfaction survey is the way to obtain user views. You can also use interviews, observation, participant observation, diaries, discussion groups, advisory forums, patient liaison officers, or a combination of any of these methods. All methods have their strengths and weaknesses and different approaches will suit different purposes.

## Have you obtained expert advice on using your chosen method for obtaining user views ?

All methods require knowledge and experience to make them operate successfully. For example, before designing a survey questionnaire it is important to carry out a number of interviews with service users in order to find out the issues that they consider important, and the kind of language they use to express their views. A questionnaire can then be designed using this material and tested out on a few more people to make sure that it is understandable and that it covers the important issues. Copying questions used by other health authorities is unwise unless you can be sure that these questions were the result of previous interviews with users.

## Are you prepared to write up and assess the success of the consumer feedback exercise after you have finished, noting any difficulties and discussing how you will proceed in order to avoid these the next time ?

You should treat each attempt to obtain user views as a learning experience, not only because this will improve future attempts, but also because the situation is not static and some problems may get worse if you make no attempt to correct them. To share this information with others engaged in a similar task will be even more beneficial, because each attempt at obtaining user views can contribute to a growing body of knowledge and expertise.

# USEFUL ADDRESSES

**CASPE Ltd**
14 Palace Court
Bayswater
London W2 4HT
Tel: 071 229 8739

**Centre for Health Economics**
University of York
Heslington
York YO1 5DD
Tel: 0904 433648/433646

**CESSA
(Centre for Environmental
and Social Studies in Ageing)**
Polytechnic of North London
Ladbroke House
Highbury Grove
London N5 2AD
Tel: 071 607 2789

**Cultural Partnerships Ltd**
90 De Beauvoir Road
London N1
Tel: 071 254 8217

**Health Policy Advisory Unit**
('What the Patient Thinks'
Questionnaire)
PO Box 344
Sheffield S1 1AZ

**HSTA Management Consultants**
Desmond Office Centre
135 Sandyford Road
Newcastle upon Tyne
NE2 1QR
Tel: 091 281130

**Institute for Social Studies in Medical Care**

14 South Hill Park
London NW3

Tel:  071 794 7793

**Research and Development for Psychiatry**

134–138 Borough High Street
London SE1 1LB

Tel:  071 403 8790

**Scottish Health Feedback**

69 Gilmore Place
Edinburgh EH3 9NU

Tel:  031 228 2167

**Social and Community Planning Research**

35 Northampton Square
London EC1V OAX

Tel:  071 250 1866

**NAWCH**

Argyle House
29–31 Euston Road
London NW1 2SD

**The Patient Councils' Support Group**

Kilbourne Street
Nottingham NG3 1BQ

Tel:  0602 484111

# REFERENCES

Age Concern. *Advocacy: Voicing the Wishes of the Older Person.* Bernard Sunley House, Pitcairn Road, Mitcham, 1989.

Atkinson Dorothy. 'The Use of Participant Observation and Respondent Diaries in a Study of Ordinary Living'. *British Journal of Mental Subnormality*, 1985; 31: 33–40.

Bernstein Richard. *The Restructuring of Social and Political Theory.* Oxford: Basil Blackwell, 1976.

Butler Kate, Forrest Mandy. 'Citizen Advocacy for People with Disabilities'. In: Winn Liz ed. *Power to the People.* London: King's Fund Centre for Health Services Development, 1990.

Campbell Peter. 'Mental Health Self-Advocacy'. In: Winn Liz ed. *Power to the People.* London: King's Fund Centre for Health Services Development, 1990.

Carr-Hill R, McIver S, Dixon P. *The NHS and its Customers.* University of York: Centre for Health Economics, 1989.

Cartwright Ann. *Human Relations and Hospital Care.* London: Routledge & Kegan Paul, 1964.

Cartwright Ann. *Health Surveys in Practice and in Potential.* London: King Edward's Hospital Fund for London, 1983. (Paperback reprint, 1988.)

Cartwright Ann, Seale Clive. *The Natural History of a Survey: An Account of the Methodological Issues Encountered in a Study of Life Before Death.* London: King Edward's Hospital Fund for London, 1990.

Clark Patricia, Bowling Ann. 'Observational Study of Quality of Life in NHS Nursing Homes and a Long-Stay Ward for the Elderly'. *Ageing and Society,* 1989; 9: 123–148.

Cornwell J, Gordon P. *An Experiment in Advocacy: The Hackney Multi-Ethnic Women's Health Project.* London: King's Fund Centre for Health Services Development, 1984.

Denzin Norman K. *The Research Act. A Theoretical Introduction to Sociological Methods.* New Jersey: Prentice-Hall, 1970.

Dixon P, Carr-Hill R. 'Customer Feedback Surveys: An Introduction to Survey Methods'. Part 2 of *The NHS and its Customers.* University of York: Centre for Health Economics, 1989.

Filstead W J. *Qualitative Methodology, Firsthand Involvement with the Social World.* Chicago: Markham, 1970.

Fitzpatrick R, Hopkins A. 'Problems in the Conceptual Framework of Patient Satisfaction Research: An Empirical Exploration'. *Sociology of Health and Illness,* 1983; 5 (No. 3): 297–311.

Fitzpatrick R, Scambler G. 'Social Class, Ethnicity and Illness'. In: Fitzpatrick et al. *The Experience of Illness.* London: Tavistock, 1984.

Gell Colin. 'User Group Involvement'. In: Winn Liz ed. *Power to the People.* London: King's Fund Centre for Health Services Development, 1990.

Goldman Alfred E, McDonald Susan Schwartz. *The Group Depth Interview: Principles and Practice.* New Jersey: Prentice-Hall, 1987.

Harris Reuben T. 'Improving Patient Satisfaction Through Action Research'. *Journal of Applied Behavioural Science,* 1978; 14 (No. 3): 382–399.

HMSO. *Neighbourhood Nursing: A Focus for Care.* London: 1986.

Hoinville G, Jowell R. *Survey Research Practice.* London: Heinemann, 1978.

International Hospital Federation. *And What Would They Know About It?* 2 St Andrew's Place, London NW1 4LB, 1988.

Jacoby Ann. 'Possible Factors Affecting Response to Postal Questionnaires: Findings from a Study of General Practitioner Services'. *Journal of Public Health Medicine,* 1990; 12 (No. 2): 131–135.

Jones Harold. 'Pulling Together in Bromley'. *Carelink,* Summer issue. London: King's Fund Centre for Health Services Development, 1989.

Jowell R, Airey C eds. *British Social Attitudes: The 1984 Report.* London: Gower, 1984.

Kaplan Sherrie H, Ware John E. 'The Patient's Role in Healthcare and Quality Assessment'. In: Goldfield Norbert, Nash David B eds. *Providing Quality Care: The Challenge to Clinicians.* Philadelphia: American College of Physicians, 1989.

Korch B, Gozzi E, Francis V. 'Gaps in Doctor–Patient Communication. Doctor–Patient Interaction and Patient Satisfaction'. *Paediatrics,* 1968; 42: 855.

Larsen D E, Rootman I. 'Physician Role Performance and Patient Satisfaction'. *Social Science and Medicine,* 1976; 10: 29–32.

Locker D, Dunt D. 'Theoretical and Methodological Issues in Sociological Studies of Consumer Satisfaction with Medical Care'. *Social Science and Medicine,* 1978; 12: 283–292.

Luck M, Lawrence B, Pocock B, Reilly K. *Consumer and Market Research in Health Care.* London: Chapman & Hall, 1988.

McCallum Nancy C. 'A Survey of the Views of Elderly Out-patients on their Physiotherapy Treatment'. *Physiotherapy,* 1990; 76 (No. 8): 487–492.

McIver Shirley. *Obtaining the Views of Outpatients.* London: King's Fund Centre for Health Services Development, 1991.

McIver Shirley, Carr-Hill Roy. 'A Survey of the Current Practice of Customer Relations'. Part 1 of *The NHS and its Customers.* University of York: Centre for Health Economics, 1989.

Morton-Williams Jean. 'Making Qualitative Research Work: Aspects of Administration'. In: Walker Robert ed. *Applied Qualitative Research.* London: Gower, 1985.

Moser C A, Kalton G. *Survey Methods in Social Investigation.* London: Heinemann, 1971.

Mulkay M. *Science and the Sociology of Knowledge.* London: Unwin Hyman, 1979.

National Consumer Council. *Measuring Up: Consumer Assessment of Local Authority Services – A Guideline Study.* 20 Grosvenor Gardens, London SW1 ODH, 1986.

National Consumer Council. *Consulting Consumers in the NHS: A Guideline Study.* 20 Grosvenor Gardens, London SW1 ODH, 1990.

Nelson Carl W, Niederberger J. 'Patient Satisfaction Surveys: An Opportunity for Total Quality Improvement'. *Hospital and Health Services Administration,* 1990; 35 (3): 409–427.

North West Thames Regional Health Authority & Industrial Training Research Unit. *Managing Customer Relations.* 1986.

Paine S C, Bellamy G T. *The Behavioural Analyst,* 1982; 5: 29–43.

Popper Karl R. *Conjectures and Refutations.* London: Routledge & Kegan Paul, 1962.

Potter Jenny. 'Consumerism and the Public Sector: How Well Does the Coat Fit?' *Public Administration,* 1988; 66: 149–164.

Raferty J, Skingsley R, Carr J. 'Preferential Insights'. *The Health Service Journal,* 1990; 22 November.

Raphael Winifred. *Psychiatric Hospitals Viewed by their Patients.* London: King Edward's Hospital Fund for London, 1977.

Roberts J G, Tugwell P. 'Comparison of Questionnaires Determining Patient Satisfaction with Medical Care'. *Health Services Research,* 1987; 22: 637–54.

Roberts Pam, Lee Nathan. 'Help Yourself to Health'. *The Health Service Journal,* 1990; 23 (August): 1249.

Robson G. 'Nagging: Models of Advocacy'. In: Barker I, Peck E eds. *Power in Strange Places.* London: Good Practices in Mental Health, 1987.

Russell E, Hunter D, Macpherson I. 'Dissemination of Research Findings: Who Wants What'. *Health Bulletin,* 1990; 48 (2): 91–96.

Sachs L. 'Evil Eye or Bacteria: Turkish Migrant Workers and Swedish Healthcare'. In: Roth Julius A ed. *International Comparisons of Health Services.* Greenwich, Connecticut & London: JAI Press, 1987.

Sang Bob, O'Brien John. *Advocacy: The UK and American Experiences.* London: King's Fund Centre for Health Services Development, Project Paper No. 51, 1984.

Shields P. 'The Consumer's View of Psychiatry'. *Hospital and Health Services Review,* 1985; May: 117–119.

Smith G D, Bartley M, Blane D. 'The Black Report on Socioeconomic Inequalities in Health Ten Years On'. *British Medical Journal,* 1990; 301: 373–7.

Social and Community Planning Research. *Keeping in Touch with the Talking: The Community Care Needs of People with a Mental Illness.* 1988.

Stewart Anita, Hays Ron, Ware John. 'The MOS Short-Form General Health Survey: Reliability and Validity in a Patient Population'. *Medical Care,* July 1988; 26 (No. 7): 724–734.

Stimson G, Webb B. *On Going to See the Doctor.* London: Routledge & Kegan Paul, 1975.

Stocking Barbara. *Evaluation for Beginners.* London: King's Fund Centre for Health Services Development, 1990.

Tessler R, Mechanic D. 'Consumer Satisfaction with Prepaid Group Practice: A Comparative Study'. *Journal of Health and Social Behaviour,* 1975; 16: 95.

Thompson Andy. *Questionnaire Distribution and Sampling.* Lecture given at 'Consumer Feedback: Exploring the Options', Seminar 2, London, King's Fund Centre for Health Services Development, 1989.

Walker Judy. *The Child's Perception of their Care in Hospital.* Lecture given at 'Consumer Feedback: Exploring the Options', Seminar 4, London, King's Fund Centre for Health Services Development, 1989.

Walker Robert. 'Evaluating Applied Qualitative Research'. In: Walker Robert ed. *Applied Qualitative Research.* London: Gower, 1985.

Ware J E Jr, Davies A R, Rubin H R. 'Patients' Assessments of their Care'. In: US Congress Office of Technology Assessment. *The Quality of Medical Care: Information for Consumers.* Washington DC: US Government Printing Office, 1988.

Winn Liz, Chotai Nirveen. 'Community Development: Working with Black and Ethnic Minority Groups'. In: Winn Liz ed. *Power to the People.* London: King's Fund Centre for Health Services Development, 1990.

Winn Liz, Quick Allison. *User Friendly Services*. London: King's Fund Centre for Health Services Development, 1989.

White Ian et al. *Hearing the Voice of the Consumer*. Policy Studies Institute, 100 Park Village East, London NW1 35R, 1988.

Whittaker Andrea. 'Involving People with Learning Difficulties in Meetings'. In: Winn Liz ed. *Power to the People*. London: King's Fund Centre for Health Services Development, 1990.

Printed by The College Hill Press Ltd (TU), London and Worthing